CHRISTIANS IN THE
AGE OF AIDS

"Finally a gap has been filled by Americans for a Sound AIDS/HIV Policy in providing a source of up-to-date, clear medical and practical information regarding AIDS and HIV for the Christian lay person. I highly recommend *Christians in the Age of AIDS* to anyone who wants a better understanding of this epidemic for personal knowledge or to help those with AIDS through the church or public education. We at ACCT will be utilizing this book as an important training tool."

Steven J. Camp
AIDS Crisis and Christians Today

CHRISTIANS
IN THE
AGE OF AIDS

Shepherd and Anita Moreland Smith

VICTOR BOOKS®
A DIVISION OF SCRIPTURE PRESS PUBLICATIONS INC.
USA CANADA ENGLAND

Scripture quotations are from the *Holy Bible, New International Version,* © 1973, 1978, 1984, International Bible Society. Used by permission of Zondervan Bible Publishers.

"Do You Feel Their Pain?" by Steve Camp, Phill McHugh, Rob Frazier and Kim Maxfield Camp. © 1988 Birdwing Music/Sparrow Song (Divisions of the Sparrow Corporation, P.O. Box 2120, Chatsworth, CA 91311/River Oaks Music Company, Administered by Meadow Green Group, 54 Music Square East, Suite 305, Nashville, TN 37203. All rights reserved. International copyright secured. Used by permission.

Library of Congress Cataloging-in-Publication Data

Smith, W. Shepherd.
    Christians in the age of AIDS / by W. Shepherd Smith, Jr. & Anita Moreland Smith.
       p.   cm.
    Includes bibliographical references.
    ISBN 0-89693-196-X
    1. AIDS (Disease)—Religious aspects—Christianity. 2. Church work with the sick. 3. AIDS (Disease)— Patients—Religious life.
I. Smith, Anita Moreland. II. Title.
BV4460.7.S64   1990
261.8'321969792—dc20   90-33967
                                      CIP

---

2 3 4 5 6 7 8 9 10 Printing/Year 94 93 92 91

CONTENTS

FOREWORD

Who would have guessed in 1981 that this mysterious new medical curiosity first known as AIDS, and caused by the Human Immunodeficiency Virus (HIV), would eventually have such an impact on American society? In my opinion, there is no question that AIDS will change our society, potentially shaking its very foundations. The chilling reality is that the ultimate impact of AIDS will depend on our response to it.

I believe history will show that America's response to AIDS in the 1980s was feeble, allowing it to escalate to a disease with global ramifications of potentially catastrophic proportions. This occurred, in my view, because of a lack of focus on fundamental medical principles, a lack of understanding of the nature of the virus in man, and a lack of leaders in the scientific and political arenas willing to risk disfavor in the eyes of some in order to save lives.

However, since 1987, Americans for a Sound AIDS/HIV Policy (ASAP), under the leadership of its founders Shepherd and Anita Smith, has helped shape a response to the HIV epidemic which—if followed widely—will effectively curtail it. ASAP has communicated a realistic view of the disease and promoted a consistent theme for policy development. AIDS/HIV policy should be based on sound medical principles, early diagnosis, compassionate care by society of those infected, and responsible actions by those infected to keep from passing the HIV virus to others.

In *Christians in the Age of AIDS*, the Smiths speak with knowledge, conviction, and authority to our society—particularly to the Christian community. Their book will help you discern fact from fiction regarding AIDS and HIV infection. You will better grasp the dynamics of the epidemic and how it will affect people. The book will also help you overcome prejudice toward persons with AIDS without compromising Christian values. This book helps improve our understanding of suffering and provides focus on the many ministry opportunities waiting; it shows us how we can grow spiritually as we confront and respond to this epidemic.

Some believe that the church is a problem inhibiting America's response to AIDS. I believe that the church provides the answers.

Specifically, the church must respond like the Good Samaritan who ministered to the wounded man on the Jericho Road, in care and compassion toward persons suffering directly or indirectly from AIDS or HIV infection. Furthermore, the church must respond by educating its young people about the danger of HIV infection and how to avoid it and other diseases through practicing sexual responsibility and drug-free living.

Many in our society have come to expect the power of science to solve any problem within just a few years. We are the polio-vaccine generation. As the AIDS/HIV epidemic grows worse and more young people lose their lives in their prime, our sense of security from technological advancements will be stripped away. Once again, like our forefathers, we will be brought back to the first principles of medicine: to treat, to comfort, and to care. One can easily see that many families will pay the ultimate price—the death of a loved one—because of this epidemic. My greatest concern is quite simple. Will we choose to blame each other, fostering hatred and bigotry? Or will we choose to come together in love and compassion as one family in crisis? Will we cast the blame on individuals we feel should have responded differently? Or will we come together as one nation in crisis to confront, challenge, and transform this crisis into a monumental opportunity.

I believe the church can lead the nation down the right path. It is time to reject the temptation of denial of the

AIDS/HIV crisis; to reject false prophets who preach the quick-fix strategies of condoms and free needles; to reject those who preach prejudice; and to reject those who try to put themselves in God's place as judge. The time has come for the Christian community—members and leaders alike—to confront the epidemic with the commitment that comes from Christ's example.

If we use all available medical knowledge, release our compassion nonjudgmentally, exploit our ingenuity, embrace our values, and demonstrate our courage to lead in the AIDS/HIV epidemic, we *will* make a difference. The AIDS/HIV epidemic is the ultimate opportunity for us to do His work—to teach *and* to heal. Our responsibility is to go forth with courage and wisdom, using the tools available today to the best of our God-given ability, and to make an impact on the HIV epidemic of the next century and its ultimate effect on our world.

ROBERT R. REDFIELD, JR., M.D.
WALTER REED ARMY INSTITUTE OF RESEARCH

ACKNOWLEDGMENTS

This book was inspired by the courage and commitment of many individuals in very diverse areas: from those struggling personally with the effects of AIDS, to those active in medical research; from people working in AIDS ministries, to legislators deliberating the issue, and people in churches across America wanting to respond appropriately to the disease.

We especially thank those relatives and friends who encouraged and supported us in founding Americans for a Sound AIDS/HIV Policy.

We recognize families afflicted by HIV infection whom we know personally. Sheila, for example, caused us to focus on reaching churches after we learned how many had turned her and her HIV-positive son away. Lauren and Nicole Burk, a mother and daughter whose family has been decimated by HIV, played a part in the establishment of our Children's Assistance Fund. The many other families and individuals touched by HIV whom we have worked with have our admiration and continued commitment.

While we have met hundreds of physicians, clinicians, and scientists active in this issue, we especially thank Dr. Robert R. Redfield and Dr. Donald S. Burke of Walter Reed Army Institute of Research for sharing their extensive knowledge of AIDS/HIV gained through studies in the U.S. military. We also thank the many speakers at our National Conferences on HIV, including codiscoverer of the AIDS virus Dr. Robert Gallo, and head of the National Cancer Institute Dr. Samuel Broder.

Our appreciation to colleagues and friends in AIDS ministries and the church. Great thanks to Dr. James Dobson and all at Focus on the Family for their support. Thanks also to Dr. Billy Melvin of the National Association of Evangelicals, who understood several years ago that AIDS would affect all denominations and who had the courage to educate denominational leaders on the issue. We recognize Dr. Tony Campolo and Steve Camp for their early vision. As well, we value the extensive ministry under Cardinal O'Connor of New York City, the many local ministries we have worked with around the country, and all Americans who respond daily to needs raised by HIV infection.

We thank those in business and legislatures who have supported ASAP and have responded in a balanced manner to offer help.

Finally, editing by LaMoyne Schneider and review and research by Wayne Elliott helped this book reach completion.

In memory of William S. Smith, M.D., M.P.H., a loving father, a caring physician, and a committed Christian whose wise counsel helped make Americans for a Sound AIDS/HIV Policy a reality.

INTRODUCTION

Our initial reaction to the AIDS/HIV epidemic was probably no different from yours. When we first heard reports of a new, virulent disease among the gay community in America, we wondered if this might well be God's judgment, as some in the church were saying.

But as we learned more about this disease and realized it would enter other populations—including the elderly, young hemophiliacs infected through blood transfusions, and infants born to infected mothers—we were forced to rethink our initial perspective. Like you, we struggled for an appropriate Christian response to this chronic disease.

The more we studied HIV infection and AIDS, the more convinced we were that the disease was a bigger issue than most people recognized in 1986 and that, sooner or later, it would affect everyone in our nation in some way. We saw this as an issue crying for the involvement of Christians. After seeking the counsel of our families and Christian friends, we formed a citizens' organization in 1987— Americans for a Sound AIDS/HIV Policy (ASAP)—to promote a medical response to this medical problem.

ASAP's goals: to conquer fear, discrimination, and ignorance of HIV/AIDS through knowledge; then to build on that foundation of understanding to destigmatize the disease, inform public policy, limit the spread of the epidemic through responsible behavior, and promote compassion for those who are infected or affected.

ASAP's approach: to educate all segments of society — health-care professionals, public policy-makers, educators, the insurance industry, the religious and business communities, and citizens everywhere — to medical facts about the epidemic; to enlighten Christians as to both the human needs and the possibilities for ministry.

By design, ASAP was not formed as a ministry to perform direct service to those infected with HIV, but rather to disseminate information and facts about AIDS/HIV to the religious community, to break down the barriers to ministry, and to facilitate ministry. We were optimistic, believing that, since we as Christians had a role in the issue, other Christians would answer a call to involvement, particularly if they were alerted to the facts and the needs.

We were motivated to accelerate our involvement after being confronted with reality during a speaking engagement in southeastern Colorado.

The conference featured a panel discussing the impact of AIDS on individuals. Sheila, a panelist and mother of an infected five-year-old, explained that her son had required blood transfusions when he was eighteen hours old. At age two, Jonathan showed initial symptoms which were diagnosed as HIV infection. When we met Sheila three years after that, the boy was getting progressively worse. In fact, she had been awake with him the whole night before the conference, not sure he would live until morning.

As Sheila related their struggles, she spoke of Jonathan's strong relationship to Jesus Christ, of how he told her that he wanted to be with Jesus, of how he prayed at night, talking about how he and Jesus would soon play together all the time. Discussing the disease's impact on the other children and on her personally, Sheila explained that one of her greatest difficulties was lack of supportive friends and neighbors. *Surely,* we thought, *a family with such obvious faith must have strong support from their local church.*

After the session, we talked with Sheila, saw pictures of handsome, bright-eyed Jonathan, and encouraged her to turn to her church for the support she was lacking. "I have gone to three churches in my town," she said. "They all told me I was welcome to come to church if I would leave my son at home."

We were stunned.

We could not get Sheila and Jonathan out of our minds and hearts. We had started ASAP a year before, had worked with members of the Presidential Commission on the Human Immunodeficiency Virus Epidemic, had sponsored conferences for health-care professionals on HIV infection and AIDS, and talked to a great many people about the epidemic. But the day we met Sheila, we reaffirmed our commitment to reach the Christian community of America.

We have sought to explain the facts about HIV infection and AIDS to churches, answering their questions and responding to their fears about the disease. Our vision is that every church in the nation be equipped and ready to respond as Christ's emissaries to persons like Sheila and Jonathan. He did not abandon them in their distress and neither must His church.

Sheila and Jonathan helped us realize that the relationship between God's judgment and AIDS was this: He would judge us by how we responded.

This book is a part of the commitment we made the day we met Sheila. It will give you the latest facts and statistics about an issue that makes headlines daily; provide a glossary of terms common in discussion of the disease; list active AIDS ministries; discuss the epidemic's impact on our nation, our communities, our churches, and each of us personally; and examine the responsibility and role of the local church and individual Christian in this unfolding epidemic.

AIDS/HIV has been called the greatest ministry challenge of our time. And we are encouraged that more AIDS/HIV ministries are being formed in the evangelical church, some of which we mention in this book. But the task is truly great. This disease is striking Americans at a rate of more than 1,000 per day. That number, multiplied by the families and friends of those infected, equals the physical, emotional, and spiritual devastation HIV disease will ultimately wreak in the United States.

We designed the book with a leader's guide and resource lists in the hope that readers will use it as the basis for a Sunday School elective or Bible study. We pray that, whether you are part of a group discussion or do personal study, our experiences and research will both challenge and compel you.

The AIDS/HIV issue is not an easy one. It touches on behaviors often difficult for Christians to deal with in light of Scripture. It calls us to account, not only in terms of how we act and react to society at large, but also of how we interact with our own families. We pray this book will enable us Christians to understand and respond to the challenge of HIV infection and AIDS as Christ would: offering healing, love, support, and redemption with outstretched arms.

SHEPHERD AND ANITA SMITH

CHAPTER ONE
The Beginning of AIDS

HIV infection and AIDS will ultimately affect every individual in the United States in some way, though the disease did not originally appear to have that potential. In contrast to the assassination of President Kennedy, man's first walk on the moon, or the release of the Iran hostages, the initial reports about this modern-day epidemic do not stand out in the American memory. News of HIV infection and AIDS—one story at a time—gradually penetrated the average American's consciousness.

But in ways similar to those great historic events, AIDS will change the face of American society and culture for decades to come. Already, more Americans have died of AIDS than died in the Vietnam and Korean conflicts. Experts predict that New York City alone will in time experience more deaths related to AIDS than America suffered in the last four wars it fought.

It is imperative for all Americans to understand this epidemic, now in its infancy, which will so dramatically alter the future of the United States and the world. For American Christians, a factual understanding about the HIV virus, the epidemic, and its impact form a firm foundation for prevention, education, and ministry, which will both limit the epidemic's reach and blunt the effects of its devastation.

The reader should understand at the outset that we will use the terms HIV and AIDS synonymously and why we will do so. HIV and AIDS refer respectively to a virus and the condition to which it leads; in this way, these terms are as distinct as cause and effect. However, since AIDS is such a highly recognized term in society; and since, at this time, all HIV-infected persons eventually die of AIDS-related illness, these two terms will be used synonymously throughout the book.

HISTORICAL PERSPECTIVE

In 1981, doctors in Los Angeles, San Francisco, and New York City began noticing a strange syndrome in homosexual men which prevented the men from mounting immune responses to illnesses which usually cause no serious effects in healthy individuals. This syndrome was identified in more and more locations throughout America as the year unfolded, particularly among homosexual men.

This Gay-Related Immune Deficiency Syndrome, or GRID as it was originally called, generated a great deal of concern among clinicians but little national publicity at the time. Not until actor Rock Hudson died of AIDS in 1985 did the disease seriously capture the attention of the American public. In the intervening years, researchers learned much about the mysterious disease, which soon was named Acquired Immunodeficiency Syndrome—AIDS.

In the first few years, theories abounded as to what could cause one's immune system to be compromised or destroyed. Many theories tied the illness's cause to homosexuality since the disease was so prevalent within the gay population. Only as scientists came to understand the disease more fully did they rule out the homosexuality causation theories. Now we know that any sexual act between an infected and an uninfected individual—homosexual or not—can transmit the virus.

After a short time, it became clear that a virus was destroying infected persons' immune systems. By 1983, the virus was identified and originally called HTLV III by American researchers, and LAV by the French. The American, Dr. Robert Gallo of the National Institutes of Health, discovered the virus coincidentally with Luc Montagnier of France's Pasteur Institute and National Center for Scientific Research in Paris.

Since Gallo and Montagnier had named their viruses in-dependently, and since a good deal of scientific prestige and royalties from the discovery were at stake, the settling of who first discovered the virus became an issue of great debate. Ultimately, the presidents of both countries re-solved the difference by declaring Gallo and Montagnier codiscoverers and renaming the virus the Human Immuno-deficiency Virus, or HIV.

Once scientists knew that the causative, or etiologic, agent HIV was the source of Acquired Immunodeficiency Syndrome (AIDS), they developed a test to find out who carried this virus. Initially, it was not understood whether someone who became infected by the virus would progress to symptomatic AIDS and ultimately die. Because relatively little time had elapsed between the discoveries of the syn-drome and the virus, scientists were uncertain what HIV infection really meant.

CLINICAL ADVANCES

Since 1983, the scientific community has had more time to study the syndrome with the additional benefit of stored blood samples from previous studies of individuals (many of whom, research subsequently showed, were infected). This large pool of data has given us a clear picture of what HIV infection means. We know, for example, that it is a progressive disease and that people who become infected will ultimately advance to symptomatic AIDS and die. Ap-proximately 10 years, on the average, is the length of time between the point of infection and death.

Research has learned that the major modes of HIV trans-mission are intimate sexual contact; the sharing of IV drug paraphernalia; childbirth and breast-feeding when the mother is infected; and blood transfusions, though now, because of the screening tests available, this is exceedingly rare.

We also know that once individuals are infected by the virus, they are infected for the balance of their lives. The virus penetrates the primary defense cells in the blood system and actually becomes a part of them. The virus' primary targets, white blood cells known as macrophages, monocytes, and T4 lymphocytes, also serve as host cells for the virus. The virus is able to reproduce inside these cells and actually convert them into virus-producing factories. Over time, one type of white blood cell (T4 lymphocytes, or T4 helper cells) is destroyed as virus reproduction continues.

Because T4 lymphocytes are the primary "foot soldiers" in the body's immune defense mechanism, the infected individual is eventually incapable of mounting a defensive response against nearly any foreign agent that attacks the body. People infected with the HIV virus consequently succumb to illnesses not often seen in the general population. Some of these illnesses include unusual forms of pneumonia, such as pneumocystis carinii pneumonia, or PCP; and Kaposi's sarcoma, or KS, a rare form of cancer. Illnesses such as cytomegalovirus (or CMV), which are not normally fatal, can kill individuals whose immune systems have been compromised or destroyed.

As a result of this knowledge, several things were done to help those infected as well as protect the uninfected. Most notably, science developed a test for the HIV virus so that infected individuals and infected blood could be serologically diagnosed. The initial test, or screen, for the virus analyzes the blood for antibodies to the virus. Once the body realizes the HIV virus is present, the immune system responds by creating specific antibodies to the HIV virus.

These antibodies have a distinct characteristic which allowed researchers and industry to develop an Enzyme Linked Immunosorbent Assay, or ELISA, to detect these HIV antibodies. ELISAs for HIV were designed to be initial screening tests, and people whose ELISAs are reactive are subject to a second series of confirmatory tests. This most often is a Western blot, which can be followed by an even more sophisticated test, such as a recombinant viral protein test.

Today's technology can accurately diagnose infected individuals with nearly error-free precision. These tests are particularly important in protecting the blood supply, since many of the original transmissions of the virus were through infected blood or blood products before these screening procedures were developed.

From a medical perspective, we have learned a great

deal about a hitherto unknown disease in a relatively short period of time. We know that, while it is not now curable, it is treatable; more importantly, HIV/AIDS is preventable because it is behaviorally driven.

THEOLOGICAL POSITIONING

While the scientific community was trying to understand this disease medically and to define its causative agent, the church was also trying to understand it theologically. Because the disease appeared in America almost exclusively in the homosexual community, some in the church believed that this was God's judgment. Pronouncements by religious leaders and debate on the issue appeared in religious media nationwide.

However, as time went by, the HIV virus infected persons in a variety of groups. Increasing numbers of hemophiliac adults and children, transfusion recipients of all ages, heterosexuals, and infants born to infected mothers were found to carry the HIV virus, causing us to rethink whether this was, in fact, a deliberate act of God toward a specific community or sin.

Debate among church members in the early '80s slowly changed to action as more and more conscientious Christians realized that God was watching their response to those in need. Denominations which accepted homosexuality and, consequently, had many infected members, were most often the first involved in direct ministry to people living with AIDS (or PLWAs).

Not until the late '80s did the churches which denounced homosexuality begin to respond in a compassionate sense to people suffering and dying from AIDS. Many AIDS ministries that began in the evangelical church were started by individuals who came out of a homosexual lifestyle. Some of these individuals were infected themselves; others were not. Yet all saw an opportunity for ministry and evangelism in this tragic epidemic. Those ministries which did reach out to people dying of AIDS found that most sought peace with God and often wanted a relationship with Jesus Christ.

Throughout the 1990s, a maturing process is occurring in both medicine and ministry. Those involved on the medical side have reached an understanding that early diagnosis and the knowledge of infection that it brings are valuable tools in offering optimal medical care as well as preventing the spread of the HIV virus to others. Those in ministry are learning that the spiritual, physical, and emotional needs for PWAs and their loved ones are great; equally great is the need to prevent the spread of this epidemic, and this can legitimately be performed in part through ministry. There has probably never been a more important time in Christian history to send a stronger message of sexual responsibility to young people. And in this case, the optimal medical response is one which complements the biblical values of the Christian community.

Contemporary Christian singer Steve Camp founded the first national religious AIDS organization to involve the evangelical community. His ministry, AIDS Crisis and Christians Today (ACCT), was born out of his conviction that Christ's love is unconditional and that the help He gave others was not dependent on or determined by how they got into trouble but only by their need. Steve's song, "Do You Feel Their Pain?" (from the album *Justice* by Sparrow) has become a rallying point for many Christians reaching out to PWAs, and its sensitivities have been similarly recognized by the secular community.

ACCT serves as networker, facilitator, and information center for Christians interested in AIDS ministry. It also works to alert the evangelical church to the full spectrum of the AIDS epidemic as it moves into more diverse communities, particularly America's sexually active youth of all races. As more and more understand that the virus cannot discriminate between sexes, ages, races, denominations, economic levels, or geographic regions, Christians' past reluctance to become involved is disappearing.

Increasingly, churches are discovering members who have become infected and must deal with the issue on a more personalized basis. Some churches, as a result, are developing policies related to HIV infection. Individual, church-wide, community-wide, and denomination-wide AIDS activities and ministries are also springing up in the evangelical church, covering a broad range of needs—from physical assistance for AIDS patients, to support groups for AIDS care-givers, to foster care for infected infants and children, to prayer support for the entire issue.

Finally, the church is beginning to realize that this epidemic offers a tremendous opportunity to let Christ's light shine brightly by helping those in need and by sending strong messages of sexual responsibility to its own members. We are beginning to understand the potential for winning a lost generation and are awakening to the significant challenge before the church.

The following chapters will provide a sound basis of knowledge by which individual Christians can make informed decisions about how to respond to the HIV epidemic, based on medical facts and scriptural leading.

INITIAL REACTIONS

The public originally feared that the virus passed from one individual to another through nonintimate, or "casual," contact. Fear of contagion understandably kept many Christians from ministry. After all, HIV infection was a new disease not fully understood; people didn't want to place themselves, their families, or congregations at risk of infection. Yet, at the same time, compassionate Christians felt the tension between those fears and scriptural mandates to care for the afflicted. Compelling data now shows that these fears, while legitimate, have not been borne out in fact. This is good news because it allows volunteers to participate in ministry without great concern for individual risk.

We will describe in detail how the HIV virus is transmitted, what the scientific community has learned about it through an incredibly intensive investigation, as well as some of the medical thinking regarding HIV/AIDS. It is also important to understand the dynamics of the epidemic; for instance, its present course and rate of spread. Many thought at one time that this epidemic would be contained to the homosexual and IV-drug-using communities. Time has shown us otherwise.

Much data is now available about the epidemic which indicates that the virus is unable to differentiate between men or women, sexual practices, races, or ages and, consequently, has spread into sexually active heterosexual populations. We will examine how data about the extent of the epidemic are significant in reaching young people in particular with strong messages of sexual responsibility.

Estimates of the number of Americans who will be infected by the year 2000 have run as high as 10 million. The potential universe for virus spread can be restricted or expanded dependent on any number of factors, including: standard public-health intervention strategies, education, behavioral change, individual knowledge of infection, and medical treatments, vaccines, or cures. We will discuss the impact of the epidemic on our society, what it means to social services, our health care system, insurance, and the economy; and construct a model of what both the church and society must do to meet the demands of the epidemic today and as it unfolds in the future.

In the Parable of the Good Samaritan, Christ named two leading religious groups of His day, represented by the priest and the Levite, who had the opportunity to help someone in great need. Neither responded. The one who actually showed compassion was an individual looked on with contempt by the followers of Christ—the Samaritan. The parable's challenge: a reevaluation of who our neighbor truly is during this plague. The AIDS epidemic is a modern health scourge which will probably know no equal, at least in our lifetime.

THE CHURCH'S CHALLENGE

Clearly, a responsibility of the church and each individual Christian is to respond in a way which mirrors Christ's actions to those who are in need and suffering. But understanding an issue intellectually, and even spiritually, does not mean that a person will respond with a parallel action. The AIDS epidemic is fraught with obstacles for Christians. Initial fear about catching the virus immobilized some and still does. For others, dealing with "those people" who became infected through sexual promiscuity and IV-drug abuse is abhorrent because such behaviors are antithetical to scriptural teaching.

We realize that not all Christians will become involved actively in AIDS ministry—just as not all are involved in prison ministry, feeding the hungry, teaching the illiterate, children's ministry, or various other areas of concern. And yet, we must see that whether or not we are actively involved in any of these specific ministries, each opportunity offers us the chance to measure our actions, reactions, thoughts, and prejudices by the spiritual yardstick of Jesus Christ's example. We will measure ourselves in these areas as we look at the ministry challenges of AIDS. Certainly God's measure of us will not be in condemning our fellowman, but in caring for him.

For those who do want to become involved in some sort of AIDS-related ministry, examples and ideas will be defined, including ministry to children, women, families, drug abusers, the sexually active, and friends of any of these individuals who are infected.

Though not generally considered so today, AIDS is every bit a family issue. Tragically, infected spouses often infect their partners. Some of these infected couples give birth to infected infants. Often, however, infected couples die, leaving uninfected orphans behind.

The traditional family structure also plays a critical role in preventing the further spread of HIV infection. It is probably the greatest barrier that exists today to the advance of the epidemic. Individuals who observe chastity until marriage and fidelity in marriage are virtually immune to sexually transmitted HIV infection. The family stops the disease by keeping it out.

The fruits of the sexual revolution stand in contrast to the fruits of the traditional family. Statistics of sexual behavior in America today, particularly among both churched and unchurched youth, dramatically show the importance of behavior change as prevention against HIV transmission. Prevention strategies are a key in this effort, and an area in which the church has a dynamic and critical role in helping control this epidemic. A truly tragic scenario is developing which could potentially result in the loss of a significant portion of an entire generation.

In light of this, Christians are challenged to look personally at suffering and how they relate and respond to it. The Scriptures teem with references to suffering, but what is suffering? Do we really understand it and its importance to each of us individually? Do we know what God's will is in reference to the suffering we see around us, and the potential suffering that may be in store for us?

These questions are important and their answers, equally so. Is there a relationship between suffering and God's judgment? If so, what does it mean in relationship to HIV infection and AIDS?

Also challenging to Christians is dealing with our own prejudices on difficult issues. Certainly HIV infection and AIDS get to the very heart of some of the prejudices Christians hold. In light of the state of our society today, can we really separate the sin from the sinner when it comes to promiscuity or homosexuality or drug abuse? Are we capable of responding as Christ did to the lepers He met and healed?

We will share our own experiences as well as the differences between personal feelings, personal prejudices, and personal responsibilities regarding a spiritual commitment. These are important issues if one wishes to become involved in AIDS-related ministry. Of these issues, homosexuality is perhaps the most difficult.

Finally, we wish to share the true cost of involvement in this issue. We believe that the only greater cost to the individual regarding HIV/AIDS is the cost of not being involved at all.

Addressing a group of church leaders at the National Conference on HIV '89, then Food and Drug Administration Commissioner Frank Young told the audience that the HIV epidemic appeared in three waves. The first wave, he said, started probably somewhere in the '50s and spread as a silent epidemic throughout various parts of the world. The second wave he named began in the early '80s with the identification of the first cases, and persists until today.

"The third wave is just beginning," he said. "And it has the potential for unraveling the fabric of our society. I definitely believe that unless we cope with this kind of infection well, it will have the capability of destroying many facets of American society. So, as this begins to unravel the fabric of our own society, it can be one of the church's finest hours or one of the church's most despicable times of hypocrisy."

All the unspoken fears and pressing issues related to the

epidemic in the future, he said, condense to how an individual views his purpose in life. "What will have to happen?" Young asked. "It will require that you not be a closet Christian. But most important you will need to synthesize your core values so you understand what is important enough to you to die for, because until you know what your core values are, you will not be able to live or deal with this disease at all."

We pray that this glimpse into the AIDS epidemic and the Christian's role in it will help prepare us all for that day so that the future of the epidemic can indeed be one of the church's finest hours.

AIDS AND
THE WORLD

CHAPTER TWO
What Are the Medical Facts?

Much of the information in this chapter is technical by nature, but it is important, nevertheless, to lay this foundation. Knowledge about HIV is critical if the church and individual Christians are to respond appropriately to the epidemic and to those infected.

A great deal of popular thought holds that AIDS is a homosexual disease. When one understands how the virus functions, though, one quickly learns that it cannot distinguish between male or female, young or old, black or white, rich or poor. One also realizes, through a thorough understanding of medical facts, how the virus is transmitted and, equally important, how it is not transmitted.

When we formed ASAP (Americans for a Sound AIDS/HIV Policy), one of the very first things we did was go to the National Library of Medicine to research the medical facts about AIDS, the virus that causes it, and how it is transmitted. Much of what is contained in this chapter is a result of that research and continuing studies we have done since. We also depend extensively on Dr. Robert Redfield of Walter Reed Army Institute of Research, who has reviewed this chapter and added pertinent information throughout. Though you may find this chapter slow reading, we hope that this basis of knowledge will serve you well in making decisions about how you or your church will respond to the AIDS crisis.

THE VIRUS THAT CAUSES AIDS

AIDS is caused by a virus known as the Human Immunodeficiency Virus (HIV). Viruses are matter which border by definition between living and nonliving material. They are actually replicable protein matter which exists in a parasitic sense and can survive only as long as their hosts exists. HIV belongs to a class known as retroviruses because its reproduction process involves the virus using its reverse transcriptase enzyme to replicate its RNA into DNA molecules. Further viral replication is then linked to the host cell's DNA.

Viruses are extremely small. Hundreds, if not thousands, of these particles can fit inside a single blood cell. Some viruses have immediate effects on the health of an individual, like the viruses which cause influenza. Others, such as the HIV virus, are slow-acting and seldom cause any immediate outward harm to an individual. While scientists have developed cures for many bacteria-caused diseases that attack the body, they have not to date been able to effectively kill viruses, though in some cases there are effective treatments or immunizations.

The focus of this chapter will be on HIV, because AIDS cannot result without infection by HIV first occurring. In fact, AIDS is really the symptomatic stage of a progressive disease caused by HIV which is largely asymptomatic, meaning PWAs do not show symptoms of illness for the majority of the time they are infected. While they are apparently well, or symptomless, they are both infected and infectious.

When former President Reagan appointed the Presidential Commission on the Human Immunodeficiency Virus Epidemic, he asked that it give him recommendations on how to deal effectively with this terrible epidemic, as well as the best ways to care for people who are infected and ill. The commission (most often referred to as the President's AIDS Commission) reported back after a year of study. The first point of the executive summary of that commission's report states: "The term AIDS is obsolete. 'HIV infection' more correctly defines the problem."

The commission said this because AIDS is only part of the problem, the tip of the iceberg, the signal that it is already too late to help somebody. We need to focus on HIV when trying to understand the total dimensions of what we are facing as a country and as a world community. The virus, then, will dominate discussion in this chapter.

In a relatively short period of time, science has learned an amazing volume of knowledge about HIV. Here's what we know.

The virus illustrated below consists of various proteins which have a distinct molecular composition. They include the outer envelope coating's proteins and the inner core's proteins. These outer and inner proteins are important because the body, in fighting off the HIV virus, develops antibodies and other cellular immune responses which match this protein composition and control the virus. Production of specific antibodies to HIV has allowed a series of tests to be developed to determine if an individual is infected. The core of the virus contains reverse transcriptase and RNA particles which, when combined with the host cells, allow the virus to reproduce.

One of the paradoxes about HIV infection is that the target cells of the virus actually become the primary host

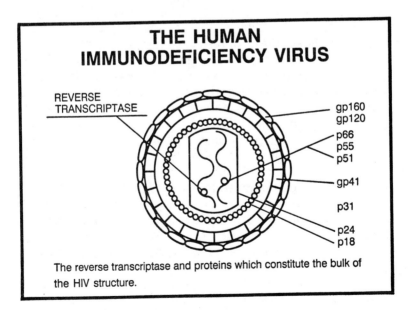

THE HUMAN IMMUNODEFICIENCY VIRUS

REVERSE TRANSCRIPTASE

gp160
gp120
p66
p55
p51
gp41
p31
p24
p18

The reverse transcriptase and proteins which constitute the bulk of the HIV structure.

cells for it. Furthermore, it is the role of these target or host cells as the body's primary immune defense mechanism to actually attack and absorb the virus. The white blood cells that the virus attacks are T4 lymphocytes, monocytes, and macrophages. The invading virus turns the monocytes and macrophages into virus-producing factories for the rest of the individual's life but does not significantly damage the host cells. Meanwhile, the T4 lymphocytes are systematically killed off over time.

The destruction of the T4 cells, the body's primary immune soldier cells, ultimately proves devastating to the individual. Normally, the T4 cells are mobilized whenever any infectious threat to the body occurs; but when T4 cells are stimulated to respond to other diseases in an HIV-infected individual, the T4 cell activation actually causes the HIV virus to replicate, and in turn, causes their own destruction. In time, a depleted T4 immune system is unable to fight off what would otherwise be non-life-threatening diseases such as rare pneumonias, or cancers, and even herpes. These are known as opportunistic diseases or infections.

The graph on page 35 charting the decline of T4 cells in a person with AIDS employs the Walter Reed (WR) Staging System. The U.S. military, through its study of HIV infection, established the progressive-stage system now widely used in the scientific community. The first stage, WR 0, designates someone who has been exposed to the AIDS virus; someone who recently became infected is in stage WR 1. Ultimately, the person with symptomatic AIDS reaches the final stage, WR 6.

This graph is of particular importance for several reasons. First, it shows that from the point of infection onward this virus does significant damage to one's immune system. While this damage is not outwardly seen for some time, the disease is progressive; early intervention to treat it is critically important. The graph also indicates that infected individuals may often be unaware of their condition through physical signs because the virus doesn't critically affect them until years after infection.

The particular individual represented by the graph, a member of the U.S. military who lived 83 months after infection, actually ran three to five miles daily and was a

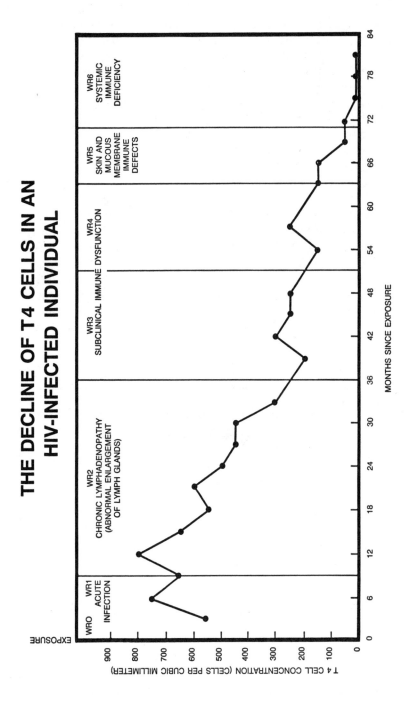

picture of good health when the first outward symptoms of disease appeared 18 months before his death. Had the individual not been tested on a regular basis, his HIV status would not have been known until opportunistic infections overcame his body's ability to effectively deal with them. This information will help scientists develop more effective treatments in the future and subsequently extend the length and quality of life for PWAs.

An interesting theory has arisen as a result of evaluating infected individuals over time. The theory suggests that the longer an individual is infected, the more infectious he or she becomes. This theory, called "dynamic infectivity," is important because it means that later-stage disease is considerably more infectious to other individuals than early-stage disease, and that we as a society become more infectious every day.

The chart below illustrates the concept of dynamic infectivity by showing the amount of HIV virus (solid line) thought to be present in an infected individual over a ten-year period. As the T4 cells, which are the antibody

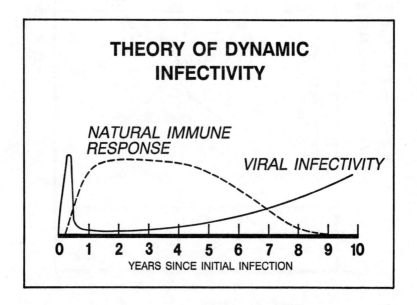

THEORY OF DYNAMIC INFECTIVITY

NATURAL IMMUNE RESPONSE

VIRAL INFECTIVITY

0   1   2   3   4   5   6   7   8   9   10
YEARS SINCE INITIAL INFECTION

response to the virus, are destroyed (dotted line), the immune system is unable to stop virus replication, and the virus becomes more prevalent in body fluids. Consequently, many researchers believe that individuals become progressively infectious. This underscores the importance of early diagnosis to prevent unwitting transmission by persons with early HIV infection.

In the past, the press and some scientific publications have reported that HIV virus is very difficult to transmit. Instances of individuals having several hundred intimate contacts with infected people, but remaining uninfected, were noted. Yet in other instances, only one intimate exposure transmitted the virus. These conflicting reports have confused the general public, leading some to believe HIV transmission is rare, while fueling fears in others that HIV can be transmitted more easily than had been publicly stated.

The data relating to the theory of dynamic infectivity helps explain both circumstances. When there were multiple exposures without infection, the contacts were probably with recently infected persons. On the other hand, when transmission occurred after only one exposure, the contact in all likelihood was with an individual having late-stage disease.

The pyramid-like illustration on page 38 was drawn from data gathered by the U.S. military. The stages WR 1 to WR 6 mark the progression from infection to full-blown AIDS. The column at the left shows the normal dropping T4 cell counts for each stage. The column at the right indicates how the total number of AIDS cases in the military study break down by stage. Typically, the later-stage cases represent a small percent of total cases; most HIV-positive persons are overlooked when attention is misdirected to symptomatic AIDS cases.

VIRAL TRANSMISSION

When the first cases of AIDS were reported by the Centers for Disease Control in June 1981, the cases involved five gay men diagnosed as having rare diseases which would not normally prove fatal in young people. However, these

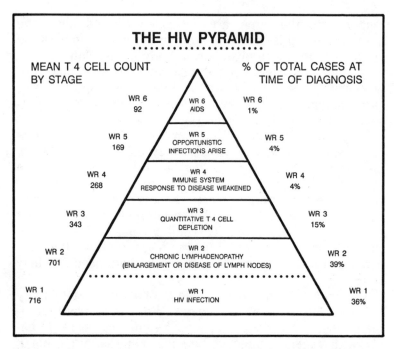

THE HIV PYRAMID

MEAN T 4 CELL COUNT
BY STAGE

% OF TOTAL CASES AT
TIME OF DIAGNOSIS

WR 6
92

WR 6
AIDS

WR 6
1%

WR 5
169

WR 5
OPPORTUNISTIC
INFECTIONS ARISE

WR 5
4%

WR 4
268

WR 4
IMMUNE SYSTEM
RESPONSE TO DISEASE WEAKENED

WR 4
4%

WR 3
343

WR 3
QUANTITATIVE T 4 CELL
DEPLETION

WR 3
15%

WR 2
701

WR 2
CHRONIC LYMPHADENOPATHY
(ENLARGEMENT OR DISEASE OF LYMPH NODES)

WR 2
39%

WR 1
716

WR 1
HIV INFECTION

WR 1
36%

individuals apparently had dysfunctional or compromised immune systems which allowed these diseases to infect them. After this report, a number of other cases were diagnosed, also primarily among gay men.

Over time, individuals who had received blood transfusions and blood products (primarily hemophiliacs) appeared among the cases reported. Then, a relatively small number of cases of drug addicts were seen, and ultimately infants and women. However, because this pattern was first seen in the gay community, many believed that the virus was somehow linked to particular sexual activity.

Consequently, the Surgeon General, among others, strongly warned against individuals participating in anal intercourse since it was believed that the trauma caused by this activity allowed the virus to directly enter the bloodstream. We now know that, while this particular sexual activity can transmit the virus, it is in no way the only mode of transmission. Studies in Africa, and now in America, show that the HIV virus is also efficiently transmitted male-to-female and female-to-male, particularly in late-stage disease. The reason for this is relatively simple.

As we mentioned before, the virus must infect particular white blood cells in order for transmission to occur. These white blood cells are found in all mucous membranes of the body and are there to protect the body from foreign agents, including the HIV virus. These mucous membranes, therefore, are the primary transmission points for the virus and are found in virtually any body orifice where sexual activity occurs. Simply put, any intimate sexual act where body fluids are exchanged can result in transmission. Thus, heterosexual relations will become the major mode of transmission in the future.

The reason that the HIV virus spread so quickly and was first seen so markedly among homosexuals was that, after it entered that community, many more opportunities existed for transmission to occur between infected and uninfected individuals than in any other community at the time. The average homosexual then had dramatically more partners than the average heterosexual. In his book, *And the Band Played On*, Randy Shilts discusses the bathhouse activity in San Francisco during the early '80s where it would not be unusual for one individual to have five or more sexual partners in a single night. For many, this pattern often occurred night after night, so the homosexual community became a veritable breeding ground for HIV infections.

The reader should remember two important points from this discussion. Point one is that HIV infection can occur when one uninfected individual comes into intimate contact (where body fluids are exchanged) either through sexual or IV means with an infected person, regardless of any specific sexual act. Point two is that transmission of the virus is actually quite difficult, if not nearly impossible, when intimate sexual or IV-drug activity does not occur. This second point needs elaboration because we were personally quite concerned about transmission, as many people might be, when we first became involved with HIV infection and AIDS.

When we formed ASAP, we knew we would eventually be working with people who were infected, and since we had a son who would soon be entering school, we wanted to be sure to do everything reasonable and responsible to protect ourselves and our family from acquiring this virus.

Perhaps the most compelling information we received on modes of transmission came from the military. After surveying more than 10,000 households around the world where at least one family member was HIV positive, the survey found no compelling evidence that the virus was transmitted other than through intimate sexual or IV contact.

Since then, we have interacted a great deal with families who have members who are infected, and in no case have we seen any evidence of HIV transmission in any other way than through intimate sexual or IV use or childbirth. This observation does not mean that a different type of transmission may never occur, but it does mean that such transmission would be exceedingly rare and would only be explicable through significant blood or body-fluid exposure. This observation also means that transmission is not going to occur through casual contact in normal church or ministry settings.

However, there have been transmissions which have occurred in the health-care setting, and these are important to look at since not all cases of transmission were restricted to needle-sticks, but could be attributed to some kind of intimate contact. For example, several health-care workers either spilled blood on cuts or abrasions, or inadvertently ingested it via the oral cavity. Another case involved a researcher who, in working with concentrated virus, acquired the infection through non-intact skin contact where the virus entered through a cut or abrasion. While these cases are rare, they nevertheless point out that people working with infected individuals should be cautious about exposure to blood.

When an individual is exposed to blood or other body fluids, reasonable precautions should be taken. Public health officials recommended that, in settings where blood exposure is likely (such as in hospital emergency rooms), workers wear rubber gloves, masks, and eye protection. Also, a 10-to-1 water-to-household-bleach solution can be used as an effective disinfectant for cleaning up after any blood or body-fluid exposure.

Remember that transmission is not going to occur in the normal church setting or in AIDS ministry, particularly if reasonable precautions are taken when required. In fact, we now have no fear in holding or hugging an infected individual, or even giving him or her a kiss on the cheek. The HIV virus is one which is not a respecter of intimate contact, but fortunately it is extremely difficult if not impossible to acquire otherwise.

In dealing with PWAs, it is important to be sensitive to their concerns in addition to your own regarding transmission. Often (if not always) people who are infected are equally concerned about not transmitting the virus to those who are helping them. One needs to be sensitive to this and not go overboard in showing unconcern about their infective status. A grandfather shared with us that he would die ten thousand deaths if he accidentally transmitted the virus to his grandchildren, and so he is particularly careful not to do anything which might expose them to it.

Moreover, be sensitive to using terminology which may be offensive to those with HIV infection. For example, people who are infected respond negatively to the term "AIDS victims" and much prefer either the term "people with AIDS," "people living with AIDS," or "people with HIV infection."

ADVANCES IN MEDICAL UNDERSTANDING OF HIV

We seem to read something new every day about HIV infection and symptomatic AIDS. While the fundamental knowledge of modes of transmission and the progressive nature of this virus are well documented, we will continue to learn more about HIV infection as time goes by.

When this immune deficiency syndrome was first recognized, a few years passed before the causative etiologic agent, HIV, was discovered. Researchers then compiled enough data to fully understand that the HIV virus was a progressive disease and that individuals who became infected would gradually become symptomatic and face near-certain death. How long a person lived was the only cofactor. The focus in the late '80s changed from symptomatic AIDS to the full spectrum of HIV disease, beginning from the point of infection onward and targeting medical therapies for both asymptomatic and symptomatic disease. With that change in perspective has come the awareness that HIV infection is less a terminal illness than it is a chronic illness.

This is particularly true with the advances in treatments for both opportunistic infections and the virus itself. Science is now focusing the development of treatments into three general categories: (1) immunotherapies which enhance the body's ability to respond to the virus itself; (2) antivirals which attack the virus directly; and (3) treatments to prevent specific opportunistic infections which otherwise kill the infected individual.

Perhaps the most exciting development of the early '90s is in the field of immunotherapies. Initial reports by the primary investigators at Walter Reed Army Institute of Research have shown that treatment with the outer protein layer, gp160, in newly infected individuals so stimulate the body's immune system that T4 cell counts actually rise. The role of gp160 may ultimately be critical in vaccine development in the traditional context of preventing the uninfected from ever acquiring the HIV virus.

Individuals who have depleted T4 cell counts but are still asymptomatic benefit from the early application of the antiviral azidothymidine (AZT). The primary draw-back with antivirals is that they not only inhibit the replication of HIV but, over time, prove toxic to the body by attacking part of the replicative process of blood production for both white and red blood cells. However, current experiments with combinations of antivirals indicate that life may be extended further during this asymptomatic period.

The treatment of opportunistic infections is also advancing steadily. Where pneumocystis pneumonia was the major cause of death for most individuals who died during the '80s of AIDS, now Septra, Bactrim, Fansidar, and inhaled Pentamidine are treating it successfully. Other opportunistic infections, such as cytomegalovirus, Kaposi's sarcoma, and others are also treatable with different medications. We will see significant life extension through the treatment of these secondary diseases, or opportunistic infections.

This is all good news for individuals who are infected, but will ultimately weigh heavily on our health-care delivery system, causing increased cost of health care for both the individual and the country as a whole—a challenge for society in the '90s.

CHAPTER THREE

Tracking the Epidemic

"Everybody knows that pestilence has a way of recurring in the world, yet somehow we find it hard to believe that one can crash down on our heads from a blue sky. There have been as many plagues as there have been wars in history, yet always these plagues and these wars take us by surprise. A pestilence isn't a thing made to man's measure, therefore, we tell ourselves that these pestilences are nothing but a bogey of the mind, a bad dream that will pass away. But, it doesn't pass away, and from one bad dream to another, it is the men who pass away."

Albert Camus
The Plague

Since ancient times recorded in the Old Testament, we have known of plagues that have ravaged mankind. Disease, especially communicable disease, has been as devastating as war itself. In fact, HIV infection has already killed more Americans than the Vietnam and Korean conflicts, and it is predicted that the total number of American lives lost to AIDS/HIV will exceed the number lost in *all* our wars combined.

It is, therefore, important to understand how epidemics in the past have run their course and what effects they

have had on society. We often work without a perspective
of other occurrences which have remarkably similar characteristics to what we are currently facing. For this reason
we should turn our attention to the past to gain a fuller
understanding of this modern-day plague.

PAST PLAGUES

Through archeological discovery and written historical
documents, we have learned that, for centuries—from
times long before the birth of Christ through the early
growth of the church, the Dark Ages, the Renaissance, In-
dustrial Revolution, and even during the 1900s—the world
and portions of it have been affected by various epidemics,
such as the Black Plague, syphilis, and influenza. These
epidemics have been spread in various ways. For instance,
rats carrying infected fleas sailed aboard ships from port
to port in Europe, bringing with them the lethal and fast-
acting bubonic plague or Black Death. Plagues have also
spread when the sneezing or coughing of afflicted individuals infected others. This is particularly true of influenza
which, in certain forms, has proved fatal to millions of
individuals. But the plague which most closely parallels
HIV infection and AIDS is syphilis.

Like HIV, syphilis is a sexually transmitted disease which
entered historical records in a dramatic way. It surfaced in
Europe about the time that Columbus returned from the New
World, and has been traced by many historians to that event,
though never conclusively. Syphilis was referred to in its
heyday as "The Great Plague." Since medicine was not very
advanced in the 16th century, many theories arose as to
what caused syphilis and why it infected people.

Many felt that syphilis was actually caused by the stars,
or the gods, or God. In fact, in Russia it was believed that
the upperclass acquired syphilis astrologically while the
lower classes acquired it sexually.

Originally, anyone touched by the disease was shunned
by society. However, over the next several centuries the
understanding of and attitudes toward syphilis changed
dramatically. Gradually scientific approaches were applied,
methods of transmission were defined, the basic cause

understood, and finally in the 20th century, a diagnostic test and cure developed. The public health measures taken to control syphilis prior to the discovery of a cure proved very effective, and limited the suffering of untold thousands.

Like syphilis, AIDS was first seen as a mysterious disease whose cause was attributed to a myriad of sources. Fortunately, we did not have to wait hundreds of years to work through a process of understanding this disease, how it was caused and transmitted. In the short years between 1981 and 1983, science was able to identify the cause of AIDS as a retrovirus, understand its methods of transmission, and a year later provide accurate diagnostic tools to identify those infected by the virus.

In spite of these unprecedented medical advances, HIV infection has escalated from a mere medical curiosity in 1981 to a worldwide epidemic involving unknown millions of people. While the crisis originally centered in certain populations, it has now shown itself to be spreading unchecked into sexually active people of all races, ages, and geographic areas.

Listed below are just some of the disease epidemics which have occurred in the United States.

1633,1648,1666	Smallpox epidemics in New England.
1663	Smallpox epidemic in New York.
1667	Smallpox epidemic in Virginia.
1668–1893	Yellow fever. There were 135 major yellow fever epidemics in American port cities during this time. The case mortality for most of these epidemics varied between 12 and 80 percent.
1675–1775	There were only two five-year intervals when the colonies were entirely free of smallpox. The main centers of infection were port cities like Boston, New York, and Charleston.

1721   During a severe smallpox epidemic in Boston, the Reverend Cotton Mather and Zabdiel Boylston began the use of variolation (smallpox inoculation), which proved highly effective.

1730   Typhoid fever epidemics began in Connecticut and South Carolina and spread throughout the colonies. Approximately 30,000 to 40,000 persons died of typhoid fever each year while approximately 500,000 were infected.

1735   One of the first modern-day outbreaks of epidemic diphtheria occurred in New England, killing 5,000 people overall or 2.5 percent of the total population. The vast majority of these victims were children.

1776   George Washington ordered variolation for every man in the American Army. The average life expectancy of American citizens at the time was less than 40 years.

1793   Yellow fever, Philadelphia. Public health measures in this epidemic depended on which theory of disease was ascribed to—either contagious (in which case quarantine was recommended) or anticontagious (in which case sanitary measures were pushed). Five thousand persons died in this epidemic. In direct response to the yellow fever epidemic, a board of health was created in Philadelphia.

1798   Edward Jenner announced that inoculation with cowpox protected the recipient from smallpox.

1802	A series of controlled experiments of human volunteers established the value of vaccination—literally, inoculation with cowpox. This was the first controlled medical experiment on humans in the United States. Effective control of smallpox depends on one factor—vaccination.
1848	Cholera epidemic. In New York City, 20,000 people were struck—8,000 of whom died. Almost 5,000 perished in New Orleans. The disease spread up the Mississippi Valley and went West with the forty-niners.
1850–1860	Yellow fever epidemic reached its peak in the 1850s, striking New Orleans hardest.
1857	Diphtheria swept Europe and America and became endemic in large cities. In New York City, the average mortality rate for this disease for a period of six years never fell below 42 percent.
1861–1865	Typhoid fever killed more soldiers in the Civil War than actual combat did.
1866–1890	Diphtheria caused 43,000 deaths in New York City.
1878	Yellow fever, Mississippi Valley. More than 75,000 people were stricken and 15,000 died in this outbreak. This epidemic of yellow fever prompted the passage of the National Quarantine Act which gave some quarantine power to the Surgeon General of the Marine Hospital Service. The act allowed him to de-

clare a quarantine but permitted local authority to overturn the decision. There were no appropriations made available for implementing this act.

1889   The New York City Department of Health declared tuberculosis to be "communicable and preventable." Public health policy was developed and implemented in 1893–1894. This was a great change from the policy followed before isolation of the etiologic agent, when the disease was assumed to be hereditary and the patient and family felt no concern for contagion.

1889   Influenza pandemic. In the United States, epidemics of Influenza A still occur every one to three years and epidemics of Influenza B occur every three to four years.

1894   Vermont reported 132 cases of polio in one year—the largest epidemic to date anywhere in the world. The death rate was 13.5 percent.

1899   Bubonic plague outbreak in New York City.

1900   Major Walter Reed identified the mosquito as the carrier of yellow fever. This meant that the disease, while transmissible, was not contagious.

1905   The last American epidemic of yellow fever struck New Orleans, causing 400 deaths among 3,500 cases. As a result, New Orleans moved to eliminate mosquito breeding grounds.

1918–1919	Influenza pandemic killed 20 million worldwide and 548,000 in the United States alone. All public health measures were ineffective, including the closing of public establishments and the wearing of face masks.
1921	Last typhus outbreak in the United States.
1942	Last outbreak of yellow fever in U.S.
1947	Influenza pandemic.
1953	Last reported case of smallpox in the United States.
1968	Influenza pandemic.
1981	First recognized cases of AIDS reported by the U.S. Centers for Disease Control.

THEORIES ON THE ORIGIN OF HIV

While it is academic at this point to know exactly where the HIV virus originated, we should discuss some theories to separate myth from reality. Many investigators believe the virus came from the green monkey in Central Africa which carries Simian Immunodeficiency Virus (SIV), which is quite similar to the HIV virus. Since monkeys represent a major food source in some areas, it is thought that man possibly ingested infected blood while preparing or feeding on the monkeys. In a mutated form, the virus was thus able to infect the humans.

We surmise this to be the most plausible theory because the epidemiological data points to Central Africa as the origin of the epidemic. One theory we have researched and rejected states that the virus was developed at Fort Detrick in Frederick, Maryland under a clandestine Army program and somehow escaped. If that had occurred, the HIV epidemic would not have begun or have been as well established as it is in Africa today. Instead, the epidemic would

have first appeared in the Baltimore/Washington area and
spread from there, which it did not.

Another theory holds that the HIV virus was developed
either by the CIA or the KGB to exterminate specific populations in different parts of the world. We have also looked
at this idea and find no reason to give it any credence. The
populations first infected do not logically fit into that scenario. In reality, while some of these farfetched notions
bear little credibility, we may never be able to say defini-
tively where or when the epidemic began.

What matters is that the epidemic is here with us and is
spreading to more and more populations all the time. As
we will see, it spreads rapidly once introduced into a community when it has numerous opportunities to be passed
from one individual to another through intimate sexual or
IV contact. In that sense, the epidemic from this point on is
very predictable.

FOLLOWING THE GROWTH OF THE EPIDEMIC

When the first cases of symptomatic AIDS were recognized
in June 1981 as a mysterious new syndrome, the CDC
carried the news in its publication, *The Morbidity and
Mortality Weekly Report*. The agency quickly received
numerous reports of similar occurrences from many points
throughout the country (most notably New York City, San
Francisco, and Los Angeles). As data began pouring into
the CDC, scientists worldwide were alerted to this problem
and, in some cases, had also seen it in their midst.

Europeans soon recognized a pattern of infections they
could trace to people who had either visited Central Africa
and had intimate exposure there or who were infected in
Europe through contact with visiting African students. At
roughly the same time, some Europeans had been exposed
to the virus in the United States, and a significant link
showing the virus being carried by individuals through international travel was confirmed.

Urbanization in Africa allowed the virus to go from city
to city and from population groups to subgroups, a pattern
which would be paralleled in the United States as the epidemic became established and widespread.

Initial significant epidemiological data came from what is known as the Hepatitis B Cohort Study of 6,700 homosexual men in San Francisco, begun in 1978. Fortunately, all blood samples taken from this group in order to study Hepatitis B among the gay population were saved. When a test for the antibodies to HIV was developed in 1985, scientists were able to go back and study the blood samples and understand how quickly the virus was able to spread among this significant number of individuals.

Research found that in 1978 three percent of the individuals in the study had already been infected with HIV. Remember that this was four years before the first cases of AIDS were identified. All these individuals were asymptomatic, showing no outward signs of sickness or disease. By 1979, the number infected in this group jumped to 12 percent; by 1980, to 20 percent; and by the time the disease was first identified, 36 percent of this group was already infected.

Infection rates among this particular study group declined dramatically in the mid '80s; nevertheless, by the end of the decade, approximately 80 percent of this group had become HIV-infected. This study affords us a better understanding of where the HIV epidemic is today and how fast it is spreading throughout America.

Beyond the San Francisco Hepatitis B Cohort, there were other significant studies in the '80s related to the spread of the virus. Because a number of homosexuals were also either bisexual or IV-drug users, the virus began to gain a foothold in the heterosexual IV-drug communities. And because the average number of sexual partners heterosexuals have is relatively small compared to the average number of partners homosexuals or IV-drug users had, the epidemic in the heterosexual community has not spread as quickly.

However, in the IV-drug community, the virus again had an ideal environment in which to be transferred from an infected individual to an uninfected individual because of the large number of persons who shared drugs and drug paraphernalia with others.

Studies among drug users in New York City showed a relatively consistent rate of infection in the '80s, between 50 and 60 percent of groups studied being HIV positive.

Sexual partners of IV-drug users soon were noted as individuals at considerable risk of infection by the virus. These individuals also provided the virus another access route to the heterosexual community, particularly to youth and young adults. One family we have worked with in New York City lost a husband, two brothers, and a sister-in-law to AIDS before the end of the '80s.

Rates of infection in other countries have also been significant. However, because of suspected incomplete reporting by many countries, understanding the spread throughout the world is quite difficult. Countries reporting to the World Health Organization (WHO) place the United States at the top of the list in both the highest rate of AIDS cases per unit population and total cases reported. The U.S., in fact, accounts for over half of all cases reported to WHO. Evidence continues to show that when multiple sexual partners or multiple IV partners exist, the virus will spread rapidly when introduced. Consider these cases.

In Bangkok, Thailand, virtually no HIV infection was seen until the mid '80s. In 1986, less than one percent of Bangkok's prostitutes (many of these individuals are also drug abusers) were infected by the virus. By 1989, the number had grown to over 40 percent—an incredible growth in just three short years!

In Nairobi, Kenya, a study was done to evaluate the susceptibility of circumcised men versus uncircumcised men to the virus. The subjects were 130 men who visited prostitutes only one time each. The study found that uncircumcised men more readily contract the virus than do those circumcised. However, over seven percent of the subjects became infected by the AIDS virus. This demonstrates once more the risk one takes when having intimate relations with individuals who are infected, and further validates that female-to-male intercourse is an efficient mode of transmission (particularly by those who have been infected for a long period of time).

HIV IN THE '90s

The growing epidemic in America is still very much misunderstood. In the late '80s, at the request of the White

House's Domestic Policy Council, the CDC began to focus on identifying HIV infection rather than just symptomatic AIDS. At the time, the primary adviser to then President Reagan was Gary Bauer, now with the Family Research Council. Bauer stated that unless we knew the extent of the epidemic, its rate of growth and its direction, we could not effectively interrupt or limit its spread, nor could we target effective educational messages. His thinking was well-founded and his stance on asking for this data took great courage since there was a strong bias against any testing at the time he made his request.

The HIV data from the CDC is still incomplete. A first phase of a sample seroprevalence study has taken place and it remains to be seen if a national seroprevalance study will ever be done. The family of surveys that is being undertaken by the CDC, while giving us information, raises perhaps as many questions as it answers because the statistics gained are not from a random sample of individuals across America, but from people visiting hospitals, sexually transmitted disease (STD) clinics, or having babies. Many who are sexually active in America neither visit hospitals, STD clinics, nor have babies.

Perhaps the best data that is still available to us regarding the epidemic comes from the military since all civilian applicants are required to be tested for HIV. What's more, because the military serves as its own blood bank in time of war, structures community-living situations for recruits, and must always maintain combat-ready troops, it has the most vested interest in understanding the virus, all possible ways it can be transmitted, and the number of people infected in its ranks. The practice of HIV testing began in October 1985, and the data gained from it gives us some significant information.

The military screens out individuals who are IV-drug users, homosexuals, and lack either high school diplomas or the motivation to serve their country. Because those applying for service do not participate in many of the risk behaviors that are associated with this epidemic, the rate of infection among the general public is thought to be three to four times greater than that for military services applicants. The following map pictures counties in which HIV infection has been found in men and women applying for military service.

**COUNTY-SPECIFIC CASES OF
AIDS AMONG MEN AND WOMEN
APPLYING FOR MILITARY
SERVICE.**

OCTOBER 1985–SEPTEMBER 1989

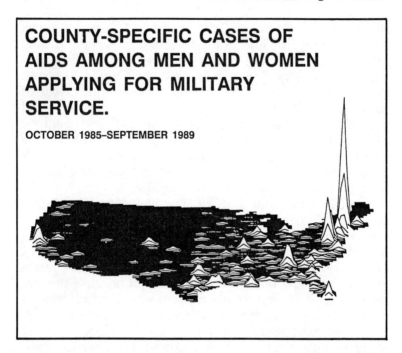

HIV infection seems to have reached the urban centers of Africa by way of the truck routes that connect them. It is interesting that in the United States, we can see on this map a similar, well-defined corridor on the East Coast along I-95, running from Miami to Boston.

What is also noteworthy of civilian military applicant data is that the older individuals are, the more apt they are to be infected. This is simply because they have a greater amount of intimate sexual activity and, consequently, more opportunity to acquire the HIV virus. In 1988, young women at age 17 had twice the rate of infection as young men the same age applying for military service, arguing for a heterosexual epidemic.

Also meaningful in the civilian military applicant data is the fact that the ratio of infected men to infected women at the end of the '80s was roughly two to one (males to females). At the same time, the ratio of men to women in symptomatic AIDS cases reported to CDC was twelve to one. This illustrates the need for understanding HIV infection rather than AIDS, since AIDS is simply a historical view of what the HIV epidemic was five to ten years earlier.

AIDS VERSUS HIV

As we have already discussed, the first point in the executive summary of the Presidential Commission on the Human Immunodeficiency Virus Epidemic report said: "The term AIDS is obsolete." The report goes on to say, "Medical, public health, and community leadership must focus on the whole course of HIV infection rather than concentrating on later stages of the disease. A continual focus on AIDS rather than the entire spectrum of HIV disease has left our nation unable to deal adequately with the epidemic. Federal and state data collection must now be focused on early HIV reports while still collecting data on symptomatic AIDS." What is the significance of focusing on HIV?

The graph below illustrates the upward curve of HIV infections beginning sometime in the early '70s, the best guess of when the HIV virus first entered the United States. The second line and shaded area in the bottom right shows AIDS cases beginning in June 1981 and running through the '80s. What this shows is that the HIV epidemic of the '70s dictated the AIDS epidemic of the '80s, and that the

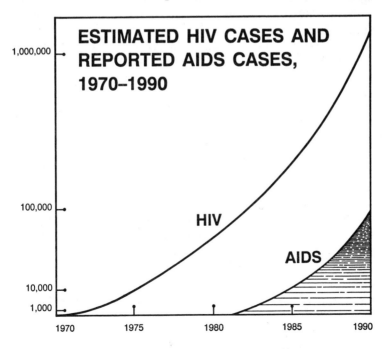

HIV infections of the '80s have largely predicated the parameters of the AIDS epidemic of the '90s. In other words, the AIDS epidemic of the 1990s has already happened.

As we saw with civilian military applicant data, the ratio of HIV infections at the end of the '80s was approximately two men infected for every woman infected, yet the symptomatic AIDS cases reported to the CDC had a twelve-to-one ratio of males to females. We can, therefore, expect the number of reported AIDS cases among women to rise dramatically in the '90s, as well as the number of heterosexually transmitted cases.

What this means is simply that we can no longer concentrate on symptomatic AIDS but must begin to focus on the full spectrum of HIV disease. We can no longer wait for statistics to tell us what happened ten years ago, and then develop strategies based on such out-of-date information.

Once we understand that the virus is our enemy and not symptomatic disease or its carriers, we must also make this understanding perfectly clear to future generations. We have sent mixed messages to our young people and must not mislead them any longer. We must make HIV infection understood, and that sexual activity outside of marriage can expose anyone to this virus and result in death.

HIV infection and the course it follows is a very serious matter. While it should be sobering to our teens and young adults, they often rationalize that science will somehow resolve this issue for us. That may be true; however, history shows us that medicine alone is not the answer. For example, despite the fact that we have had a cure for syphilis since 1945, today we are experiencing a significant syphilis epidemic throughout America.

We cannot afford to wait, depending on science for an answer. Since HIV infection is a behaviorally driven epidemic, modified behaviors can end it. We hope in all sincerity that a vaccine will be found to prevent new infections from occurring and that cures will be found to relieve the suffering of those already infected. However, we cannot stand by hoping this will happen. We must help those who are suffering while we prevent our young people from becoming future sufferers and ultimately statistics in this epidemic.

CHAPTER FOUR

The Future of AIDS

One day we will all be able to look back and see clearly how the HIV epidemic spread across America, as many epidemics have in the past. Few experts, however, have been able to look into the future to see how this epidemic will spread. The one notable exception is Dr. Robert R. Redfield of the Walter Reed Army Institute of Research.

Dr. Redfield's predictions about this epidemic have been uncannily accurate: that this is a progressive disease and that early diagnosis was in the best interest of the patient and society. We will depend on his expertise in much of this chapter to look at the future of this epidemic. In 1984, Dr. Redfield also argued that the virus could be spread bidirectionally (that is, from man to woman, or woman to man) and not solely within the homosexual community, as most people at the time felt. In all cases, Dr. Redfield's understanding of the epidemic has been proven correct.

Having established a good understanding of the virus and how it is transmitted, we will not surprise you in predicting at this time the future of this chronic disease.

INFECTION RATES

The bulk of data acquired to date has been primarily about symptomatic AIDS cases. The data we do have on HIV infection shows us that the epidemic flourishes until it reaches some point of saturation in certain communities. Within the homosexual community, that point is as high as 75 to 80 percent of its population. Within the IV-drug community, the saturation point can be 50 to 60 percent, if not higher. Among hemophiliacs, it is as high as 90 percent. As many as 80 to 90 percent of prostitutes have been found infected in some study populations.

Obviously, once infection rates reach such high proportions, they can no longer continue to grow by high annual percentage rates. Therefore, reductions in rates of new infections in these communities may not be marks of educational success or of our ability to control the epidemic. In fact, such high rates of infestation exhibit our total failure to control this devastating disease.

Johns Hopkins Hospital in Baltimore and Bronx Lebanon Hospital in New York City have annually surveyed individuals entering their emergency rooms. Both hospitals have seen increased infection rates and increased numbers of sexually active young people showing new infections.

The Johns Hopkins data showed that its three-percent infection rate in 1986 jumped to six percent in 1988, an increase of 100 percent. The Bronx Lebanon study showed an increase between 1987 and 1988 from 13 percent to 23 percent. It is not surprising, then, that during certain months in 1988 and 1989, one infant in six born at New York City's Lincoln Hospital had an HIV-positive mother; nor is it surprising that 30 percent of black males between the ages of 25 and 44 entering a hospital in Newark tested HIV positive. It is not surprising, but certainly very sad.

Without editorializing on what a disappointing commentary this is on our country and its response to this epidemic, we affirm the need to look objectively at the epidemic's growth in order to accurately anticipate future needs, since they will be so considerable.

PEOPLE'S REACTIONS TO HIV

In times of crisis, people have historically made well-defined, recognizable psychological responses to their situations, reactions which have four distinct features. First, when an epidemic such as AIDS/HIV strikes, people do not want to believe it can happen; they do not want to believe it can happen to anyone they know; and they certainly don't want to believe it can happen to them personally. This is called denial. The response of denial on the part of any community affected by the epidemic plays a critical role in our ability to treat the spread of HIV infection. As long as people indulge in denial, it will be difficult to halt this monster in its tracks.

Then, once people see the effect of HIV infection in the flesh, they enter the second phase—anger. They become angry at the loss of a friend or the suffering of a relative or the unfairness to them personally in what is happening around them.

The third and critical phase is acceptance. Once the reality of the situation becomes apparent and people realize there is no way to turn back the clock and change what has happened, acceptance occurs and allows for a rational understanding to take place.

Only then can the fourth phase (which is positive response to the crisis) occur. Communities have organized to help those who are suffering, to educate those who are not infected on ways to avoid infection, and have formed support groups for those providing care or volunteer help. These communities have redefined AIDS as a chronic illness rather than merely a fatal disease for which nothing can be done.

We believe that those communities most heavily infected have gone through all four phases—denial, anger, acceptance, and positive response— and the church at the end of the '80s has struggled through the first three phases. The challenge for the church of the '90s will be to take the fast track on the fourth phase of positive action.

To illustrate this phenomenon of denial, I (Shepherd) would like to share an incredible set of events. They caused me to realize that the heterosexual community, like the homosexual community before it, will rationalize that such a tragic infection could never happen to it (even though the ratio of infected men to infected women in Africa is nearly one to one, and the ratio from the civilian military applicant data is roughly two to one). People's ability to rationalize is absolutely remarkable and, combined with denial, can be very dangerous in the face of HIV infection.

Anita and I were driving back East from visiting ministries in the Los Angeles area in the summer of 1988, and planned to go through several different states to visit state legislators, ministry representatives, and others involved in this issue. The interstate from Los Angeles to Salt Lake City took us through Las Vegas where we stopped for breakfast at a hotel whose marquee welcomed "Lifestyles '88" to town.

Anita and I went in for breakfast but my natural sense of curiosity brought me by the registration desk billboard, which detailed more specifically what Lifestyles '88 was—the national convention of swingers throughout the United States. In case you are unfamiliar with this group, as we were, they are heterosexual people who swap partners for sexual pleasure. This was a real eye-opener.

Because of our concern about AIDS, and quickly understanding the transmission opportunity the virus would have in such a community, I set out to find the head of the group. After some time, I was able talk to this man, a Ph.D., about the issue of AIDS. He asked me if I thought it could be transmitted heterosexually. I deliberately gave a nebulous response since I didn't want to alienate him from talking at some time in the future. He responded that had I answered in the affirmative, he would have labeled me "an enemy," since it was obvious to him that AIDS could only be transmitted between homosexual men.

I was quite shaken since I had somehow felt that heterosexuals would view HIV infection differently from homosexuals and that the sexual obsessions among heterosexuals were not as great (which shows you my own biases and prejudice). Obviously, I was wrong.

On leaving that meeting, I probably passed 300–400 people lined up to register for this convention (of a total 2,000 expected); to my amazement, they looked like folks in any other community in this country. There was nothing unusual about their appearance that would have aroused suspicions that they participated in this lifestyle. Some looked wealthy, some looked less affluent; but any of them could have been your next-door neighbors or mine. So what does this tell us about the future of the epidemic? Simply this:

1. The epidemic will continue to spread unabated once it gains a foothold in heterosexual communities where

multiple intimate sexual activity or IV contact occurs.

2. The epidemic will spread less quickly in communities that have fewer multiple opportunities for transmission to occur. However, since there are numerically many more heterosexuals than homosexuals or IV-drug users, the total number of people that may become infected is very significant.

3. The epidemic will not spread among people where both partners abstain from sexual relations until marriage and are faithful in that marriage (unless they contract the HIV virus through a transfusion or unusual accident in the health-care environment).

4. The epidemic will ultimately affect everyone in America and will cost our country and our world exceedingly.

SOCIAL AND ECONOMIC IMPACT OF THE EPIDEMIC

Due to the severity of this epidemic on the future of America, people may refer to "the time before AIDS" or "the time after AIDS." It is increasingly common as we travel to hear stories of individuals and churches who never thought they would run into this terrible disease but who have already had to deal with in their own families or congregations. The common denominator in most of these stories is how dramatically HIV infection has changed individuals' lives—how they will always remember their lives being fractured by the invasion of AIDS.

Depending on the eventual size of the AIDS/HIV epidemic, the nation will be affected either moderately or severely in a myriad of ways. In order to understand the significance of HIV versus other diseases, remember that HIV strikes primarily young people.

The Centers for Disease Control evaluates causes of death by weighting them against retirement, in a formula called YPLL, "years of potential life lost." The formula subtracts the age at death from 65 and adds the balance cumulatively to each disease listed. Heart disease and cancer rank at the very top of this list and their rates change very little over time, as do other causes of death. It is uncanny, actually, how stable this chart is year after year, considering the hundreds of thousands of years in the leading categories. In fact, most causes of death on an annualized basis change very little in total years of potential life lost.

The exception to this rule is AIDS/HIV. Between 1984 and 1986, long before significant numbers of AIDS deaths had occurred, the ranking for this disease jumped from 13th to 7th on this important scale. Within a short time, it will approach heart disease and cancer, becoming the nation's third leading cause of death, when evaluated by YPLL. And if no considerable change in the course of this disease takes place, AIDS will lead all causes of death as we enter the 21st century.

What does the loss of many of our young people mean to our aging society? First, let's back up and view the big picture without AIDS/HIV. As individuals live longer in our society and our birthrate declines or levels off, America as a whole will grow older as measured by the average age of Americans living at the start of the 21st century. This aging of America in itself places demands on our health-care system, as well as on other services—tax impact, loss of tax base from income earners, and the loss of people in the labor force to provide services in skilled labor.

Now, if we compound the social overload caused by the aging of America with a disease that could cut down thousands of young and middle-aged tax payers, professionals, and service providers, we face a large problem indeed. Public services for individuals suffering from HIV infection—housing, meals, and even transportation—will deplete public resources. But who will pay taxes to support programs like this? As increasing numbers of young people become ill and eventually die, the tax base that they represent will impact federal revenues negatively. While these young people will not be a burden in later years from a retirement benefits perspective, they will represent a loss of revenue in the not-so-distant future.

Furthermore, the unskilled labor market will be impacted most heavily; at first, as this disease will tend to disproportionately affect low-income individuals in America, driving up hourly wages; and then further adding costs to everything from housing to food.

The epidemic can turn productive Americans into AIDS

patients whose health-care needs are tremendous. The Army estimates that the average cost of carrying an infected patient from time of infection through symptomatic AIDS is approximately $250,000. The hospital requirements of AIDS patients are significant and largely unpredictable. Estimated costs for this care for 1990 approach $5 billion and could grow to over $10 billion by 1993, when AIDS cases in that year alone may exceed 100,000.

Increasingly, improved treatments and hospice programs are being developed that will not require AIDS patients to be hospitalized in many instances. Still, a growing number of people will need some hospitalization. The elderly will be among the first of the uninfected to feel the weight of this impact, particularly in the larger epicenters of the epidemic, such as New York City and San Francisco. In some instances, the demand for hospital beds will be so great that space will simply be unavailable for the very ill.

In addition to the demand for services, other areas of the economy and day-to-day life will also be affected. Insurance industry estimates range as high as $50 billion for AIDS-related claims for the '90s. Consequently, insurance companies have already begun protecting themselves against claims from HIV infection by now screening many applicants for the virus. As the epidemic spreads, insurance companies are broadening the areas in which they test for HIV; they are also lowering policy-size limits for which testing is required on life insurance and requiring most individual health-insurance policyholders to be HIV-free. Companies that have not tested for HIV in potentially high-infection areas face possible insolvency, though fortunately most companies took action rather quickly to protect themselves against losses.

These changes in the insurance industry do not mean that a large number of individuals will become ill without insurance benefits. However, a significant burden will fall on public financing of health care, potentially raising everyone's tax liability. We will increasingly see uninsured risk pools established by states, and the federal government taking action to provide treatment centers for persons infected. This process will be spurred by the increase of symptomatic individuals who, to date, have been very outspoken in their demands for health-care benefits.

THE '80s RESPONSE TO AIDS/HIV

The epidemic struck two culturally diverse groups in the
'80s, at least in symptomatic disease. In fact, no two
groups could probably be further apart than the white,
male homosexuals and the largely homeless, inner-city, minority, IV-drug abusers. Likewise, the responses to date
have been quite different, depending on the communities
affected, and will change further as the epidemic continues
to spread to even more communities.

The homosexual community rallied around this issue
like none other in its recent history. It is quite remarkable
that such a devastating event could have so many positive
results for this community. AIDS became a reason for or-
ganizing groups of homosexuals in cities throughout America and for receiving funding for services and education
related to the epidemic. The Gay Men's Health Crisis in
New York City received $1.5 million in federal grants in
1987 alone. Many of the support systems in cities where
the virus has been present the longest, however, are disin-
tegrating under the weight of growing numbers of individuals becoming symptomatic and ill. Many who were volunteers in the past now find themselves in the unfortunate
position of having to be the receivers of care themselves.
The overtaxing of support systems and volunteers will
reach crisis proportions in the first half of the '90s for
most of the heavily infected homosexual communities in
major cities.

Many inner-city IV-drug users, on the other hand, were
not accustomed to receiving health-care benefits, are not
organized or united as a group, and to date have not
placed a significant demand on traditional health services,
with the exception of the use of the emergency room
(which is often used as a primary access point to health
care). Local health clinics have felt the weight of IV-drug-
related cases, but most often HIV epicenters show a dramatic need for expanded emergency-room facilities.

Due to this demand, individuals with non-AIDS-related
emergency needs are not receiving immediate treatment.
For example, New York City passed a law in 1989 requir-
ing hospitals to treat emergency-room patients within eight
hours of admittance. The number of people having to stay

overnight in one New York City hospital emergency room rose from an average of under 10 a month in 1986 to over 700 a month in 1989.

The general population (by that, we mean primarily the heterosexual community) has seen only small numbers of individuals become symptomatic from HIV infection. However, these figures are increasing and, in fact, are the most rapidly rising statistics of AIDS cases reported to the CDC. As the epidemic spreads, we will see heterosexual AIDS support groups arise similar to those developed by the homosexual community in the mid '80s. Some of these community-based organizations have already been established, and the seeds of local AIDS ministries in many communities are now also taking root.

THE '90s RESPONSE TO AIDS/HIV

The epidemic of the '90s will differ dramatically from that of the '80s in that those affected will increasingly be heterosexual, mostly black and Hispanic initially, and eventually more and more young individuals of all races. The effect this will have on society will depend on how effectively we curtail new infections and how successfully science develops effective treatments, vaccines, or cures.

Though the church was reluctant to become involved in this issue and spent a great deal of the '80s arguing whether AIDS was or was not a judgment from God, it will now play a significant role in the resolution of this epidemic in the decade of the '90s for two reasons.

First, churches across America will begin to see more and more HIV-positive individuals in their congregations. Because this disease will no longer be outside their sphere of experience, they will have to educate themselves and react appropriately.

Second, many Christians will come to view this epidemic as an opportunity rather than a crisis, an opportunity to show the true meaning of God's love through action, to be Good Samaritans, to let God's light shine through them as they help others.

"It's clear to me that there is absolutely no way that this nation will find a way to alter its priorities rapidly enough to be able to adequately respond to people with HIV infection," says Dr. Robert Redfield. "So, one has to turn to an institution where it is not inconsistent with their basic philosophy to promote concepts of compassion, concepts of giving, concepts of care. I believe that the religious community in America will ultimately determine our success or failure in responding to this epidemic.

"The church's response to promote by example, through the works of God and not just the words, must all be provided in the context of unconditional love and nonjudgmental human dignity. This poses a challenge to all of us. The church's role will determine whether we win or lose. To date, we have failed to accept our responsibility to challenge the virus with the vigor, the courage, the commitment, and the compassion we're capable of. We need to exploit our ingenuity, to embrace our values, to demonstrate our courage, and to persevere through the next decade."

AIDS AND THE CHURCH

CHAPTER FIVE
The Ministry Challenge

Though most of us paid no attention to AIDS until its death toll skyrocketed to astonishing numbers, few Christians missed the church's initial response to AIDS in the early '80s. Conservative fundamentalist preachers led the charge; they countered one New York City bishop's assertion that AIDS was not God's judgment on the homosexual community by stating unequivocally that it was.

Concerned about such unproductive debate, Chuck Colson asserted in an editorial titled "Who Speaks for God?" *(Jubilee,* January 1984) that, whether or not AIDS was God's judgment on a specific sin, each individual had a responsibility to respond in love as Christ would to those suffering. He cited as an example one of Prison Fellowship's staff members, ChristyAnne Collins, who regularly visited hospitalized AIDS patients.

"Ironically, while the bishop and his conservative challengers were pontificating over who was responsible for AIDS, I discovered that a young woman on my staff named Christy was using her evenings and weekends to do something about it," Colson wrote. ". . . .Christy and her friends remind us of a great truth: The quiet, often unnoticed actions of 'ordinary' Christians who believe *and* obey speak far more loudly than all the bombast of so-called religious leaders."

In our search for a proper personal theological perspective, we concluded that HIV infection, like other sexually transmitted diseases, is a consequence of people's sinfulness. If mankind had followed the guidelines established in Scripture regarding sexual responsibility and care for one's body, there would be no sexually transmitted diseases or drug abuse. However, when we violate God's laws, consequences result. In the case of AIDS, those consequences not only include significant pain and suffering, but also death.

Speaking to religious leaders on AIDS, Ron Sider of Evangelicals for Social Action said: "The Bible everywhere teaches that God is both loving and just, both merciful and holy, and, therefore, has established a moral order in the universe. Ignoring God's law structured into nature has consequences. . . . This is not to say that the AIDS virus that only recently emerged is some supernatural divine creation to punish homosexual practice. I reject that. On the other hand, I refuse to bow to today's widespread relativism and deny or ignore the clear biblical teaching that some things are wrong no matter what Hollywood or Greenwich Village says. Ignoring the moral order of the universe has consequences."

We don't have to look far to see the consequences evidenced by the AIDS epidemic. We see devastation from infection in the homosexual and IV-drug-using communities and rising infection rates in youth who ignore risk by being sexually active. Like the protagonist in Albert Camus' *The Plague*, we also see the suffering of those not directly involved in risk behaviors. For instance, HIV disease is affecting newborn infants through their mothers; the elderly, young hemophiliacs, and others through blood tranfusions. Camus wrote that a loving God could be neither so cruel nor so inexact, and concluded that his main character must respond to others in need. His reasoning: that judgment was a form of cowardice, inaction was morally wrong, and only service with compassion pleased God.

The HIV epidemic presents the church with the opportunity to theologically wrestle through emotions and beliefs that are at the core of our selves and our faith. That process, though at times burdensome, enables us to mature spiritually. The balance of this book will deal with some of the difficult issues that accompany the epidemic to which believers must respond appropriately.

THE CHURCH'S RESPONSE TO AIDS/HIV

"The evangelical church has embarrassed me by the way in which they have reacted to AIDS patients," Dr. Tony Campolo told a group of Christians in Dallas on World AIDS Day 1989. "You say, 'You don't understand. That disease came from sin.' Biblically and theologically all disease comes from sin. And all of us will die from some kind of disease.

"I am upset with an evangelical community that treats these sick people like the Pharisees treated lepers 2,000 years ago. What the Pharisees wouldn't do for the lepers, Jesus did do. He embraced them, He loved them, and He said, 'The whole world can call you unclean; I'll go on loving you.'

"If God embraces these people, then how dare His church reject them? If God loves these people and won't turn away from them, then how dare anybody that calls themselves a follower of Jesus do otherwise?

"We Christians don't realize what we're up against with this disease that is taking so many lives. If we get up on our high horse and stay away from it, we will have lost the opportunity to express what God is all about. Compassion. I am not trying to explain. I am not trying to justify. I am simply declaring that there is a God who loves people and will go on loving them. And we who are His people must love them too."

Dr. Campolo is correct. And we see evidence that the church of Jesus Christ is awakening to its responsibility to apply His love to this issue. More and more Christians are beginning to care. The crowd Dr. Campolo addressed on December 1, 1989 was 3,700 strong, gathered to hear Steve Camp and other Christian singers. But they also came to the event to learn more about AIDS.

The call to involvement usually doesn't materialize instantaneously. The first step is to listen carefully to God through prayer and Scripture. The Bible is full of examples of people who listened to God before taking action or becoming involved in a particular issue. From Noah and Esther to Daniel and Paul, we learn the importance of taking time to understand God's principles before acting. Scripture also offers insight into those who understood God's principles yet failed to act accordingly.

The debate about judgment must end. No individual or court could impose a worse sentence on persons who become infected than that which they receive through contracting this disease. The judgment that must be considered is how God will judge each of us in our response to this modern plague.

The second step to involvement is a thorough understanding of the virus, its disease, and how it is spread. Those in the church who foster fear of rather than knowledge about AIDS serve neither the church nor themselves. Fortunately, some of this fear has been abated; but we continue to see Christian materials on AIDS whose primary focus is protecting "us" from "them." In our view, this attitude not only limits God, but it undermines His ministry. God's holiness will not be compromised by extending mercy to those who suffer, regardless of how they came to be in that state.

The preceding chapters have dealt with the medical knowledge we have today about the HIV virus itself and how it is transmitted. We have learned that the virus cannot differentiate between individuals or even sexual acts, but will be transmitted only when an infected individual comes in intimate sexual or IV contact with an uninfected individual. The virus will not be transmitted through caring for those in need. Certainly, common sense dictates certain precautions be taken when ministering to HIV-infected persons, but they need not be excessive or irrational.

Once a congregation or individual has gained a thorough understanding of the disease process, they need to evaluate whether God would have them participate in helping stem this epidemic. We recognize the needs in many areas of society—various addictions, illiteracy, child abuse, the homeless, the homebound, the hungry, and many others who are hurting in some way. God calls different people to work in different areas; therefore, each individual in the church must thoughtfully pray and seek guidance as to whether he or she should become actively involved in the AIDS issue.

Once the individuals and congregations commit to the AIDS issue, they can evaluate what is most important and how to be most effective. This will be determined in part by the resources available and the surrounding environment. It may be appropriate for one person to provide hot meals for PWAs, for another to offer child care to HIV-positive mothers, and for yet another to assist infected persons with applications for financial assistance for medical costs. Looking at the needs of the community, a church may decide to begin an AIDS hot line, open a hospice, or provide training for members wanting to assist PWAs.

From our experience with AIDS and the evangelical church, we feel that there are two fundamental ways to curtail suffering and the spread of the epidemic. The most obvious is responding to individuals who are symptomatic or HIV-infected. The other, equally important, is preventing new infections. While ASAP is a medical/public-health-based organization, our personal commitment to God through Christ requires that we respond not only to what is best medically, but also to what God would want us to do.

The optimal medical messages in dealing with this epidemic coincide precisely with what we discern as the appropriate biblical response. For example, the optimal medical message regarding sexual responsibility is for young people to be abstinent until marriage and then faithful in marriage. The optimal medical message regarding treatment of PWAs is to respond compassionately, as if responding to anyone with a serious illness.

In the Old Testament, the five books of Moses established proper codes of behavior in relation to sexual practices. These are reiterated in the New Testament with a significant focus on relational responsibilities between husband and wife. Christ is emphatic when He states that sexual activity outside of marriage is wrong—not only actions, but also thoughts about such actions. So we must arm ourselves in practical and responsible ways in talking to young people and single adults about sexual responsibility. This will be discussed in more detail in later chapters.

The needs of this epidemic are twofold. First, the next generation of young Americans can either carry the legacy of AIDS or the legacy of love. That is both the challenge and the opportunity facing the church.

Second, the church must respond to those who are HIV infected or suffer from symptomatic AIDS. We receive calls daily from PWAs throughout the United States, many of whom are in churches already, some of whom are ministers or elders. They are looking to us for help since they don't believe they can find it in their churches. By reading this book, you have taken the first step in being able to offer these people the kind of support and care God intends the body of Christ to provide.

COMPASSION AND ACTION

When writing a book, one struggles not only to give birth to the content but to find the fitting title for it as well. Naming the book may sound like a simple matter, but the process, nevertheless, took considerable time and thought. One title we believe would have captured the personality of this book equally well is *The Road to Jericho.*

The Parable of the Good Samaritan is probably the most compelling in Scripture related to how we should treat PWAs. When asked in Luke 10 how people could attain eternal life, Jesus said to love the Lord with all one's heart, soul, strength, and mind and to love one's neighbor as oneself. The question, then, becomes, "Who is our neighbor?" Christ's example involves an individual much despised by the Jewish community He was addressing—a Samaritan. The priest and the Levite ignored the wounded man they passed on the road, but it was the Samaritan—the distained one—who truly served God by helping that injured person.

By using this example, Christ removed the issue of judgment from the equation and said that we must do to others as we would have them do to us. This is simple but not easy. The church to date has already written some sad chapters responding to HIV infection.

We are reminded of the Ray family in Florida whose three hemophilic sons became HIV infected through taking the Factor VIII product they needed to survive. The mother sought help from her minister to cope with the tragedy. But in the mid 1980s, the conservative church community in America felt that the AIDS epidemic was a judgment by God and those infected should be shunned.

So, rather than seeking competent medical advice, her minister expelled the family from the church. In doing so, he made it clear to his congregation what he was doing and why, and that this family should not have church support. By this action, he clearly identified the family and their problem to the rest of the community which, at the time, created dramatic problems for them. The family had to move to another location where, fortunately, they were accepted.

We find it ironic that many non-Christians have been doing the accepting and many Christians have been doing the rejecting. Lately this trend has been reversed in large part and we hope will be totally eliminated as we speed through the '90s.

DEALING WITH TOUGH ISSUES

Probably the toughest part of dealing with the AIDS epidemic is understanding the community where it first spread. Because most Christians not only have a strong bias against homosexuality, but against homosexuals as well, this task is even more difficult. It is important to separate the sin from the sinner.

We all do things that displease God, but few of us do such things that label us outwardly as a particular kind of sinner. Homosexuals have that dubious distinction, which no doubt inhibits many Christians from becoming involved in this issue. Dealing with people who are IV-drug users is equally difficult for most churched people.

For many who have grown up in the faith, such statements may seem nearly blasphemous, since it almost sounds like we are saying one should embrace homosexuality or drug abuse. That is not our intent. What we are saying is that anyone who is involved in this issue will be challenged to examine his or her own faith in relationship to these and other issues. Some Christians find this hard, while many find it challenging and rewarding.

The *Christian Herald* interviewed Richard Schubert when he was president of the American Red Cross. Because of the responsibility of the Red Cross to the nation's blood supply (donations, donors, blood recipients, and overall blood supply), Schubert had to deal very forthrightly with the issue. He said that he felt individuals had to view this epidemic in the terms that virtually anyone can become infected, regardless of who he or she is, but more in relationship to what he or she did.

A devout Christian, Schubert stressed that there were difficulties related to ministry and involvement. Regarding concerns about transmission in a ministry setting, he said that while the dangers were incredibly small, believers should not expect risk-free lives following Christ.

Dick Schubert and others saw individuals of many persuasions responding to this epidemic, but very few Christians. Fortunately, the church is working through its legitimate role in questioning from a theological perspective why the AIDS epidemic occurred; it has concluded largely that AIDS is not a specific judgment, but rather a reflection of how far mankind is from following God's commands. John 8:31-32 talks about being set free; but Christ first requires us to follow His commands and become His disciples before the truth sets us free. Yes, these are challenges, but more than that, they are great opportunities.

MINISTRY OPPORTUNITIES
WITHIN THE EPIDEMIC

When the epidemic first unfolded in the early '80s, the primary ministry opportunity then was to the gay community in America. A number of ministries founded to help people leave the homosexual lifestyle were confronted with AIDS. Some of these spawned AIDS support groups which, in turn, have grown into full-fledged ministries themselves as the epidemic has matured in the homosexual population.

Ministry opportunities have expanded with the epidemic. One of the first to recognize this was Sonny Oliver who works with Teen Challenge in Rehrersburg, Pennsylvania. Sonny directs a residential center for 200 men involved in substance abuse. The program, which has a 70-percent success rate in turning drug users into productive citizens, includes Bible study and vocational training. At any given time, between 5 and 30 percent of the center's residents are HIV positive. These men are fully part of the program but they receive counseling about AIDS and how to keep from transmitting it to others.

We have enjoyed working with Sonny and Teen Challenge at a national level to examine what HIV and AIDS mean to their ministry today and in the future. Persons involved in this ministry not only have to equip themselves to fight the battle, but also to seriously educate communities that support them about the need. We hope as you read this book and begin thinking about committing yourself to an AIDS-related ministry that you will consult family, friends, and others in your church to enlist their prayer and support, and to educate them to the issue.

A third arena for ministry is infected mothers and infants. Because the public health effort has not focused on the HIV status of adults considering having children, even in high-incidence areas, many mothers give birth not knowing their own HIV status. If the infants show no outward signs of the disease, these mothers continue to be unaware that they themselves are infected. Some of these will pass HIV on to their babies—who might not be infected—through breast-feeding. As a result, we are seeing many infants born with HIV—a sorrowful legacy of this epidemic.

In New York City, for example, the number of women giving birth to HIV-positive children reached nearly 1 in 50 by the end of the '80s. Though all are HIV positive at birth because they carry their mothers' antibodies, only about one third of HIV-positive infants go on to carry the virus and acquire AIDS.

The average life span of an infected infant ranges from 18 to 36 months. Often these children already show symptoms of illness at birth and never leave the hospitals where they're born. Many mothers, on learning of their children's illness, simply leave them and never return. These babies have become known as "boarder babies" since they are boarded by the hospital their entire lives.

Ministries are being established to take these infants into homes where they are cared for and loved for the duration of their short lives. The advent of antiviral treatments for infants brings hope that these children will live increasingly longer. The work for those who take on responsibility for AIDS children is difficult, but the rewards are great. The care-givers need the support of churches and to know that others are praying for them.

AIDS also afflicts young people who are not infected

when it kills one or both of their parents. Finding other
relatives to help take care of the children is often difficult.
Eventually, the epidemic may become so devastating within a family that no one will be left to care for the children
orphaned by AIDS. For this reason, ASAP started its Children's Assistance Fund, designed to help families whose
parents have been stricken.

One special family from Pennsylvania we have worked
with has appeared on the cover of *Life* magazine (July 1985)
as well as numerous television AIDS specials. The husband, a
hemophiliac, and his 18-month-old son died several years
ago of AIDS. The wife, who is HIV positive, is heroically
fighting not only for her life but—most importantly to her—
for her surviving daughter, who is not infected. Young people
whose parents have AIDS suffer dramatically. The church
can decide whether their futures will be brightened by love
and acceptance or shrouded with suffering and rejection.

Another area of opportunity (one which will become in
time the greatest field for ministry) is among heterosexuals
who become HIV infected. All signs today indicate that we
will experience a significant heterosexual AIDS epidemic.
The need for support is growing because many heterosexuals who seek information and assistance, in minority and
nonminority communities alike, are reluctant to call their
local community-based AIDS organizations because those
groups are predominantly homosexual.

AIDS organizations are beginning to arise and provide support to heterosexuals. Many are and can be church-related.

Those who do AIDS-related ministry today unanimously
agree that the greatest need of the infected individual is
spiritual. The love of Christ will provide solutions to the
stress, isolation, and devastation that accompanies this
disease. We can all offer this love by following Christ's
model.

Steve Camp, Christian singer and founder of ACCT,
points to the story of Christ's healing a leper in Mark 1:40-
42 as the pattern for biblical response: Jesus was approached, He was moved with compassion, He touched the
leper, and then met the need. "The Lord's response was, 'I
am willing,' " Steve says. "We can be approachable, have
compassion, and even 'touch' them, but until we are willing to serve them, they remain unchanged.

"How many times are we quick to quote John 3:16, but slow to demonstrate 1 John 3:16? 'This is how we know what love is: Jesus Christ laid down His life for us. And we ought to lay down our lives for our brothers. If anyone . . . sees his brother in need but has no pity for him, how can the love of God be in him? . . . Let us not love with words or tongue but with action and in truth' " (1 John 3:16-18).

CHAPTER SIX

Most-asked Questions about AIDS Ministry

Q: Will AIDS really impact me and my church?

Experts say that by 1995 everyone in the United States will know of at least one person with AIDS. In December 1990, the number of AIDS cases reported by the CDC went over 150,000, with more than 60 percent having already died—a number which tragically will double very quickly. From the time the CDC began data collection on AIDS cases, their doubling time has been 20 months on average. If that trend continues, there will be more than 200,000 AIDS cases in the United States by 1993. This number does *not* include those infected with HIV, since the CDC has no accurate data on HIV infection; estimates run between one and one and a half million people, however.

Based on this information, most churches in the nation by 1995 will know of at least several people with HIV disease, a good number of the infected being in their own congregations.

The epidemic is already starting to affect Christians across the nation. Jeannie, a young professional woman, attended a concert sponsored by ACCT to raise awareness of AIDS in the Washington, D.C. Christian community. "We sang the song, 'Do You Feel Their Pain?' with Steve Camp over and over," she said. "When I left the concert with my friend, I said, 'I haven't felt their pain. I don't know anyone with AIDS. I don't know how a person with AIDS feels.' "

Within six months of that concert, Jeannie had seen a coworker and a longtime friend die of AIDS-related diseases. Because of confidentiality issues at her workplace, Jeannie didn't go to her pastor with questions but instead came to ASAP. Nationwide, Christians like Jeannie have already dealt with HIV infection and AIDS, often without telling their Christian friends or pastors.

Q: I read different statistics on the number of people infected. Who has the most accurate information?

The number of people with symptomatic AIDS quoted by the CDC is considered as accurate as possible because it is based on actual cases reported to that agency by each state's public health department. The CDC acknowledges that this number is underreported by 10 to 20 percent— others say by 30 to 50 percent—because not all persons with AIDS are diagnosed, and at times attending physicians do not record the cause of death as AIDS-related.

Statistics on HIV infection vary widely. Prior to 1990, HIV infection was not reportable to the CDC. Though the CDC has developed a system to track HIV infection data, figures will be unreliable because all 50 states do not require the reporting of HIV infection. Until all states report HIV infections accurately, estimates will vary widely. Today estimates are based on various mathematical models that project figures of AIDS cases, and on a series of studies which test blood for antibodies to HIV.

The U.S. Department of Health and Human Services estimated HIV infections at one to one and a half million in four consecutive years, 1986–1989; the agency then gave a "best guess" of one million for 1990. Other studies estimate infection to be anywhere from one to three million.

The reason for such discrepancy on HIV statistics is the way HIV infection and AIDS have been approached in the United States. Early concerns about confidentiality and discrimination kept the medical community from encouraging testing for those at risk for infection. Not until the end of 1989 did the American Medical Association vote to make mandatory the reporting to public health officials of HIV cases. Because of the length of time that passes from initial infection to the onset of symptomatic AIDS, we know that the AIDS cases we see today represent infections which occurred in the late '70s or early '80s.

Without accurate statistics on the number of people with HIV infection today, we have no way to calculate the number of AIDS cases in coming decades. Even taking the lowest estimate of HIV infection would mean that in the decade of the '90s, we can expect one million more people to be diagnosed with AIDS. From all indications in recent serological studies, actual infection rates are closer to the midrange of the estimates.

Q: How do I know whom to believe and whether ministry to people with AIDS will put me at risk of contracting the virus?

Many in the religious community discussed ways that HIV can be transmitted, unfortunately going to occasional extremes. Some contend that the virus can be passed through means other than the exchange of blood and body fluids, and childbirth and breast-feeding when the mother is infected. Suggested modes of transmission have included: mosquitoes, handshakes, toilet seats, doorknobs, sneezing, public transportation, and food prepared by HIV-positive persons. Rather than providing accurate knowledge, this discussion has often kept Christians from ministry by feeding fears. We find it interesting that most who propagate these views are not medical researchers or physicians and have not worked directly with AIDS-patient research, diagnosis, and treatment.

When we founded ASAP, we too had questions about accurate medical information and researched sources of reliable data, the most reliable of which we found to be from the U.S. military. After also researching HIV extensively in medical journals, we approached Drs. Robert R. Redfield and Donald S. Burke of Walter Reed Army Institute of Research because their articles evidenced a thorough understanding of the issue. Both Redfield and

Burke involved themselves with HIV since the earliest days of research, participating in Robert Gallo's study of the virus, diagnosing and treating thousands of persons with HIV infection, and studying their spouses and families through long-term follow-up.

While military data does not always support CDC's statistics on AIDS cases and estimated HIV infection, it agrees completely with CDC's stated modes of HIV transmission: exchange of infected blood or body fluids through sexual or IV contact; and childbirth and breast-feeding when the mother is infected. To date, all medical evaluation of the epidemic that Walter Reed Army Institute of Research has given us has proven accurate and solid. The institute finds no evidence to support so-called "casual transmission" of the virus via toilet seats, hugging, handshaking, food preparation, mosquitoes, and the like. In addition, the follow-up with families has shown no transmission from infected persons to other family members other than through sexual intercourse or sharing IV-drug paraphernalia.

Based on these findings from the best medical experts we have found, there is no reason to believe that anyone would be put at risk for contracting the HIV virus through ministry situations. No one need worry about transmission occurring through HIV-infected persons attending church services, by inviting them home as dinner guests or overnight guests, or in other typical ministry settings which might occur. The biggest risk is to the HIV-positive person whose immune system is suppressed or even depleted. Infected persons are, thus, susceptible to the common viruses present in any social setting, such as colds and influenzas.

There are some very specific situations which could pose risk to uninfected persons:

☐ From time to time HIV-infected persons suffer from opportunistic infections which might be contagious to others, such as tuberculosis.

☐ Some HIV-infected persons become infected with cytomegalovirus, which can pose some risk to pregnant women, causing miscarriage or birth defects.

☐ Persons coming into contact with body fluids of infected infants (for example, in a nursery setting) should wear gloves and comply with CDC guidelines for disinfecting and cleanup of toys and equipment.

☐ Any incident which involves possible contact with infected blood, such as nosebleeds or cuts, should also be dealt with using gloves and CDC guidelines for cleanup.

Again, these are special situations, most of which do not arise in typical ministry settings, but of which we should all be aware.

Q: Will I or my church get a bad reputation by ministering to people with AIDS or encouraging them to attend our church?

Though this fear has kept some Christians and churches from becoming involved with PWAs, it is difficult to support this fear based on Scripture. Certainly our Lord didn't worry that His reputation would be tainted by His ministry to those not accepted by the society of His day. Scripture repeatedly explains that the Pharisees, Sadducees, and even Jesus' disciples objected to the settings in which He ministered. His response was consistent: "It is not the healthy who need a doctor, but the sick. . . . For I have not come to call the righteous, but sinners" (Matt. 9:12-13).

You may find that some Christian friends look at you askance when you first get involved with ministry to PWAs. We were criticized by some who didn't understand why we felt we should become involved in a problem fraught with sinful behavior and stigma. But our commitment to Christ compelled us to follow His leading and His teachings regardless of what others might think or say. We hope that one day those Christians who are not following Christ's example by reaching out to people with AIDS or other needy people in their communities will be in the minority.

Q: Why should I or my church become involved with an AIDS-related ministry when there are so many other needs to meet in our society?

We do not disagree that the demands for ministry on individual Christians and local churches are great. Indeed, without Christ, all of this would be impossible. But no amount of apathy and ignoring the issue will change the reality. We will all have to face the epidemic sooner or later. Because of prior ministry demands, Christians sometimes fail to recognize the incredible need. To list social issues which cry out for church involvement is easy: homelessness, drug abuse, racism, fractured families, runaway teens, and on and on. There is a common thread that will eventually weave itself into each of these problems: AIDS. No matter what ministry you feel called to, you will sooner or later encounter AIDS in that context.

We would never suggest that Christians and local churches drop other ministries and begin AIDS ministries. Many local churches are already stretched to their financial and human-resource limits. What we must do, however, is heed the call to compassion and recognize the reality of AIDS. By gaining knowledge of the issue and creating an atmosphere in which those affected feel accepted enough to share how AIDS has touched them, we can minister to needs in their lives without numerous additional programs or resources.

Q: I have had no experience with homosexuals or IV-drug abusers. How can I be effective in AIDS ministry?

Historically, the church has ministered to people in all sorts of situations. We don't have to experience homelessness to minister to the homeless. We don't have to be former inmates to minister to those in prison. It's not necessary to have suffered an emotional breakdown to assist those in emotional distress. Likewise, we don't need firsthand experience with behaviors that put people at risk for contracting HIV to minister to people with AIDS.

Obviously, knowledge about specific behaviors and experiences assist in our understanding of another's struggles. We must gain all the knowledge and training we can to minister effectively in any situation. But the requirements for ministry to anyone, including PWAs, are compassion, sensitivity, a nonjudgmental spirit, and a recognition that the most anyone can be is a sinner saved by God's grace.

Q: In my community, the only people involved in this issue are homosexuals and people who don't share my faith in Christ. How can I work with them when I totally disagree with their worldview and motivations?

Before assuming that you don't agree with the perspectives of those in your community involved in the AIDS issue, take the time to learn which organizations are active and what services are offered. Many Christians who feel called by God to serve PWAs find, first, that there are already other Christians involved, and second, that they can learn from and cooperate with others, even though they may not share a common faith.

Jack Larson, founder of Masterworks International (a ministry in the Dominican Republic to establish schools and churches and to treat HIV-positive children), is a volunteer to AIDS patients under the chaplain in a Florida hospital. The chaplain's volunteers represent a number of churches and beliefs. One fundamental difference between Jack and the other volunteers is their views on homosexuality. Whereas Jack believes homosexual acts are called sin in Scripture, the others see them as an acceptable alternative lifestyle. "I let them know what I believe and we have some lively discussions," Jack says. "I realize that if I want them to allow me to state my opinion, I must allow them to state theirs. Our common goal related to the patients is mercy, letting them know Jesus loves them."

When Jack decided to get involved in the hospital program, he knew he would be challenged by those who disagreed with his theology on the AIDS issue. He studied Scripture to thoroughly think through his position before any discussions. "I've learned to be secure enough in my own faith that I don't feel I have to actively evangelize them all, but can back up my beliefs with Scripture," says Jack, pointing out that there are appropriate times to take a stand and also times not to participate. For example, he has not put his name on a printed brochure related to the chaplain's ministry containing statements contradicting his view of Scripture. He also feels he could not actively join a group whose foundations or stated purpose were inconsistent with his own theology.

There are innumerable ways to be involved with PWAs

whether or not you decide to participate in groups with whom you may not share faith. Opportunities include volunteering to visit AIDS patients at a local hospital or nursing home; volunteering at a local sexually transmitted disease clinic; or visiting HIV-positive inmates at a local jail or prison. Certainly praying for those infected and those caring for them is helpful as well. One blind woman who wanted to help now calls homebound AIDS patients each day so they have someone to talk to.

Q: How can we start to address the issue in our local church?

The place to start is education and prayer. Very few of us want to become involved in anything that we don't understand. The church holds a position of trusted leadership on social and spiritual issues. As such, it is a logical source for AIDS/HIV information for its members. The local church can provide accurate information while offering a forum for discussion in which members feel comfortable, accepted, and able to share their questions and fears.

Church leaders can raise AIDS awareness by mentioning it in sermons, raising AIDS-related prayer requests, focusing on health-care issues — including AIDS — related to home and foreign missions or health-care professions in the local congregation. Some denominations have issued statements or produced materials which could provide a starting point.

Church members interested in researching and presenting information can form panels to address the congregation on such topics as: medical facts, education issues, legislation updates, and ministry ideas and methods.

A congregation-wide HIV education/awareness campaign can be planned with special presentations for youth and adults including: medical facts, perspectives on human sexuality, information on drug abuse, confronting death and dying, and caring for those who are ill or grieving. These sorts of education programs can be designed to fit into regular Sunday school or youth group programs and be extended over a period of time.

Whether or not a congregation decides to provide an

organized HIV-awareness program for the entire membership, one issue that must not be overlooked is prevention
education for young people. We cannot assume that our
youth understand everything about AIDS if many adults do
not. Programs that explain the medical facts and help
teens understand the importance of responsible behavior
related to sex and substance abuse are critical to protecting the coming generation.

Q: Should my church adopt a formal AIDS/HIV policy?

National religious groups and denominations are increasingly adopting statements on HIV. In general, these statements explain the groups' understanding of the epidemic,
how HIV is transmitted, who will be affected, and what
members' responses should be. Unfortunately, most local
congregations do not address the topic until it affects
them.

The best approach is for any congregation to meet the
issue through education and/or policy before members become ill. Church members must have their questions answered and fears put to rest before they will be ready to
become involved.

Education provides the foundation for any policy development on AIDS. Any written church statement should be
the culmination of an HIV education program for the entire
congregation, drafted from an informed stance and an atmosphere in which attitudes and fears have been
addressed.

Some congregations decide no separate policy is needed
regarding AIDS. Others develop general statements calling
for compassion and care. Still others are more specific in
terms of sacraments and theology. The type of policy a
church adopts, if any, will be determined by local attitudes
and needs. It is critical, however, that polices adopted not
exclude an infected member, but that they are in accord
with accurate medical facts and reflect God's love.

In the mid '80s, Peter Pendell and the Millington Baptist
Church in northern New Jersey were surprised when they
learned someone in the congregation was HIV infected.
Finding no other churches that had dealt with AIDS and

could offer assistance, the congregation struggled to head off the fears of uninfected members while ministering to the infected family. "I have regrets about the way we handled the situation," Pastor Pendell says. "The way we introduced some of the restrictions we imposed was a crushing blow to them, and the very restrictions we imposed kept us from ministering to them effectively."

The family ended up leaving the church for one which was more open to them. Based on this experience, Pastor Pendell believes that facing AIDS in the local church offers "an unparalleled opportunity to intercede and intercept fears in a way that only the love of Christ can address. Our next step," he says, "is to go find AIDS patients we can minister to and not wait for them to come to us."

Pastor Fred Martin in Bemidji, Minnesota did not know anyone with AIDS. Feeling, however, that his congregation needed to address the issue, he began mentioning it in sermons and formed an AIDS task force to look at policy. Over several months, the entire membership was involved in discussing draft policy statements while voicing concerns and fears. The result was a policy statement which was adopted by the congregation.

"The important thing about policy is not necessarily what gets written down on paper," Pastor Martin reflected, "but the process the congregation goes through in discussing the issues. What will happen when a person with AIDS comes to our church? I expect more members will take an interest then. That will be the real test of our AIDS policy and our Christian faith."

Another pastor, realizing that the child of one of the church families would probably come home for care near the end of his bout with HIV infection, initiated an AIDS education program for the adult membership to begin preparing them to accept this individual—and others who might be infected—into their fellowship.

Suburban, affluent McLean Bible Church in McLean, Virginia was surprised by AIDS. The son of a longtime member approached Pastor Lon Solomon with the news that he was HIV positive. The pastor didn't know where to turn or what help to offer. Before long, another HIV-infected person came to the church for help. "It was a life-changing situation for me and our church," says Solomon.

"I believe before it's all over that God's going to do that [bring someone with AIDS] to virtually every church in America. Pastors probably already have people in their congregations who are HIV positive and either don't know it or are petrified of telling anyone for fear of being rejected."

Q: I am concerned about AIDS and want to get involved, but my pastor and church don't share my concern. What can I do?

Opportunities are all around for you to be involved in the issue individually. Certainly, you can pray about the epidemic at large and seek out ways to serve in your community. There are also a number of AIDS ministries which can provide information and opportunities to assist.

Pastor Lon Solomon suggests three things someone can do before his or her church is ready to address AIDS. First, prepare for the day when the church will want to get involved. Become trained in practical ways to do ministry. Second, ask the pastor for permission to lead a group of volunteers interested in AIDS ministry. Put an announcement in the bulletin to find others interested in the issue. Third, actively pray that God would remove obstacles in your church to getting involved and that the church leadership team will get the vision for AIDS ministry.

"I believe that the local church is woefully unprepared to deal with the AIDS crisis," Pastor Solomon says. "What we'll all see in the next five to ten years will totally overwhelm most local churches, and to some degree, already has. We're already behind the curve. But I'm not discouraged about that because I believe God is leaving us a wide-open door if we have the courage to step through it to minister."

CHAPTER SEVEN

Ministry Models

If anyone had told us five years ago that we would be working with AIDS education and service today, we would have written him or her off as definitely "touched." Not that we have ever been reluctant to be involved in challenging social or ministry issues, but discussion about AIDS was vague then and very unappealing. It was an illness that no one really understood, that affected only a few people (most in communities where we had no contact), and none of our friends had been taken ill. How easy to ignore something so far removed from one's own experience.

Even when we felt God's nudge to become actively involved with the issue, it was not because we had seen AIDS-related tragedy firsthand. We didn't know anyone who was infected at that point. It was the conviction that, as God's people, we had to do something about a problem that so clearly had the potential to have a stranglehold on America economically, socially, physically, and spiritually that finally made us take action.

Today, no one could convince us to stop working with the AIDS issue. We have made precious friends, some who are infected and others who are affected by the virus. They are people from different parts of the country, from various backgrounds and professions, of all ages and races, each related to the AIDS issue through his or her unique circumstances.

For American Christians, the epidemic visible today and foreseeable throughout the '90s offers opportunities for ministry to every age-group, all races and ethnic groups, and all geographic points in the country. At the same time, the epidemic provides vast opportunities to become involved regardless of one's gift. There is a need for prayer for those affected by the epidemic, just as there is the need for volunteers to visit hospitals, provide hot meals for those afflicted, or provide foster or adoptive care for children infected or orphaned. And there is always need for spokespersons to talk about AIDS/HIV to raise their churches' consciousness about involvement. This epidemic has given everyone in the American church today a chance to minister, regardless of age, experience, or gift.

This chapter will outline some particular ministries targeted to those affected by the epidemic. In addition, we will discuss some general ways to perform ministry even before you know someone with AIDS in your community or church.

LEARN, PRAY, BEGIN

To repeat what we said earlier, the first steps to becoming involved in AIDS-related ministry are knowledge and prayer. As you have learned through the first few chapters of this book, HIV infection and AIDS are complicated medical conditions which manifest themselves in a variety of ways. The most effective way to pray for or deal with an infected individual one-on-one is to understand what that individual is facing. This approach is not unique to this epidemic; but because infected persons will go through a number of medical stages where they will experience particular symptoms and physical manifestations, ministry volunteers need to understand what to expect.

For example, Christians in AIDS-related ministry must be ready to face the disfigurations that sometimes accompany Kaposi's sarcoma without flinching or backing away. We must be ready to face without fear the loss of weight and strength that will eventually come. We must be ready to see our brothers and sisters with AIDS through the times when they are unable to eat properly because their bodies reject all forms of nutrition. We must be ready to face the sight of medical equipment, needles, and tubes without hesitation. We must be able at times to lift those suffering from the deepest depths of depression.

We are not trying to scare anyone away from AIDS ministry. On the contrary, we welcome as many as are called to involvement. But we don't want to pretend that it will be easy. It is never easy to deal with the basic issues of life and death, suffering and pain. And AIDS often brings a lingering, exhausting, painful death.

Those of us involved must be prepared from the outset to follow through to the end. It won't help for us to be there offering PWAs Christ's love at the beginning only to abandon them when they near death. Ministry to people with AIDS — or to anyone — is a long-term commitment that Christians must enter responsibly and with clear vision of what lies ahead.

INDIVIDUALS WITH NEEDS

Infants/Children
By the end of 1989, more than 1,800 children under age 13 had been diagnosed with AIDS since the CDC began keeping statistics on the epidemic. By 1991, the number of newborns infected with HIV is expected to rise to 20,000[1], an infection rate which some experts predict will mean one of every ten pediatric hospital beds in America will be filled by an HIV-infected child. To date, these infants born to HIV-positive mothers are concentrated in epicenters of the epidemic (see chapter 3).

The unique thing about this youngest group of HIV-positive Americans is that not all of them will develop AIDS. Between birth and 18 months, as we stated before, about 70 percent of HIV-positive infants will lose all traces of HIV antibodies. These noninfected newborns test positive at birth only because they carry their infected mothers' antibodies to the virus.

Older children, while not infected with HIV, are touched by the epidemic nonetheless. Experts estimate that in New York City alone, between 50,000 and 100,000 children in this generation will lose at least one parent to AIDS. According to Dr. Pauline Thomas of New York City's Health Department, by 1995, 20,000 uninfected orphans will need either adoption or foster care.[2]

These children, most of them black or Hispanic, are becoming part of an already overcrowded foster-care and adoption system. Those who are infected are classified as "special needs" children, and enter a system where approximately 60 percent of the foster-care caseload and children available for adoption nationwide are already in the "special needs" category. Only about one third of these will be adopted in any given year; others are left in hospitals as "boarder babies," and still others are sent to group facilities.

Joyce Pilotti, a mother of three from northern New Jersey whose former husband died from AIDS, was led by God to found Arise and Shine Ministries to assist special-needs children in finding help. Her goal is to identify Christian families to serve as transitional homes for children in the foster-care system. She calls them "branch homes" — after Scripture's vine-and-branches metaphor — and their function is to provide Christian care for either children whose mothers may be hospitalized or in drug rehabilitation programs, or who have been orphaned and will go on to be adopted.

Arise and Shine Ministries supports other ministries like the Walter Hoving Home and Teen Challenge by placing the children of those involved in their rehabilitation programs. Joyce's hope is that the idea of "branch homes" will be replicated across the nation as a way of extending Christ's love to the children of AIDS.

Vivian, a grandmother in the Northeast, provides foster care for several HIV-positive babies. She has two in her home now and would like several more. Since starting this personal ministry, Vivian has seen one child die of AIDS and another go on to become totally healthy and find an adoptive home.

Ministry to these children is today needed primarily in America's large northeastern cities and states where infection is highest but will eventually be required in other locations. An individual or church can help these children by:

☐ Assessing local needs related to HIV-positive infants and orphaned children.

☐ Learning how the state foster care and adoption systems work, specifically related to "special needs" children. Laws vary significantly from state to state.

☐ Volunteering at local hospitals or homes for "special needs" children to learn their needs firsthand and to understand what is involved in ministry.

☐ Opening one's home or those of other church members to foster or adoptive care.

Churches can provide support for its members who are involved in this ministry by assisting with child care, donating baby supplies, or subsidizing adoption fees.

Teenagers

Most young adults who contract AIDS will have become infected in their teenage years. Since it takes so long from the initial infection to the onset of AIDS, most teens will not see peers who are sick. Further, if teens see none of their friends dying of AIDS and if they have the typical adolescent feelings of invincibility, they will not perceive any serious risk from AIDS or any other devastating problem. This is common of denial for this age-group.

Though during most of the '80s teens did not account for a large percentage of AIDS cases, studies in 1989 began showing that HIV infection among teens was escalating. Experts have said that teenage infection "will be the next crisis" and that it is spreading heterosexually among males and females equally. Signs indicate that teenagers today "are like homosexual men at the beginning of the AIDS epidemic: the number of full-fledged AIDS cases is relatively low, but there are abundant signs that the HIV is spreading."[3]

To date, AIDS ministry to teens has centered primarily on prevention education. Josh McDowell Ministries, the Institute for Teen AIDS Prevention, and others have concentrated on giving teens skills to refrain from premarital sexual activity and drug abuse in order to avoid contracting HIV.

The future teenage AIDS epidemic predicted by experts is already visible in some teen populations. Covenant House, an international child-care agency for homeless and runaway youth, ministers to "throwaway" kids in major metropolitan areas of the United States. Early in 1986, the New York City Covenant House staff began noticing symptoms of HIV infection. In a 1988 study of 1,111 youth who came through Covenant House, 7 percent of those ages 16–21 and 17 percent of those age 21 were HIV positive.[4]

According to the National Network of Runaway and Youth Services (NNRYS), an estimated 1.3 to 2 million homeless children live in the United States. Many of them subsist through survival sex; some share IV needles and sex with other runaways whom they view as family.

The NNRYS has developed strategies to educate runaway and homeless youth to their risk for HIV.

There are difficulties with HIV prevention and care programs for teens. Not enough treatment facilities exist for adolescents using drugs which are linked to HIV transmission, adolescents are not included in current government clinical trials for AIDS-related treatments and drugs, and the natural history of HIV in teens is not well established.

Christians can support ministries to homeless and troubled youth through donations and volunteer efforts. But a key to the teen epidemic of the future is prevention education. Surveys consistently report that American young people get more information about sex from pornography than they do from parents or their churches. Christian parents and churches must play a role in giving value-based sex education to young people if we are going to save the next generation from AIDS.

Drug Users

Of the AIDS cases reported to the CDC through 1989, 18 percent of male cases were traceable to IV-drug use; 52 percent of female cases were due to IV-drug use. While the problem is widespread, it is accentuated in the inner city and minority communities.

One of the best ways to prepare for this ministry is to be educated about drugs and symptoms of drug use and addiction. To help educate its members, the local church could invite ministries dealing with drug abuse to present drug-and-ministry seminars at church home missions conferences or in special ministries focus programs. Ministries helping people overcome their drug addictions are also helping curb HIV infection as a result.

Apart from building local awareness and networking with existing ministries, Christians need to be open to helping those struggling with long-term addictions.

Homosexuals

Due to the way the AIDS epidemic started in the United States, a disproportionate number of homosexual men accounted for 66 percent of the cases among men at the end of 1989. Already this figure is declining and, in the '90s, this will not be the profile of the symptomatic AIDS epidemic. But for the coming few years, the church will continue to see more homosexual men with AIDS than any other group in society.

The first evangelical ministries to see AIDS and respond were those already in place in the gay community, helping to heal sexual brokenness and bring gays out of their lifestyles. Most of these AIDS ministries, which initially served homosexual men, are expanding as the epidemic spreads to include other populations.

The issue of homosexuality stops many Christians from caring about PWAs. We have set up a hierarchy of sin (which is preached as if ordained by God) in which homosexuality is worse than other sexual sins or those of greed and slander, even though Scripture groups them all together as wicked in 1 Corinthians 6:9. Believers usually accept heterosexual promiscuity and adultery as "less sinful," yet these sins appear alongside homosexuality as behaviors not pleasing to God.

Please do not mistake us. We are not saying that Christians must buy into society's attempts to make homosexuality an acceptable alternative lifestyle. Not at all.

What we are saying is that we must stop making homosexuality the unforgivable sin. One Christian man in the Midwest voiced the widespread attitude in the church community today: "I can have compassion for the hemophiliac with AIDS because he didn't do anything to get it, but I really can't feel the same way about the homosexual with AIDS." The way Scripture reads, we dare not harbor a "they deserve it" attitude toward any particular group, for we equally do not deserve our Saviour's love and are in danger of being judged by our own standards.

The AIDS ministries which began primarily as outreaches to homosexuals have done an excellent job of developing ministry models that can be replicated in any church or community across America. Many offer training for volun-

teers who want to work with AIDS patients. (See list at the
end of the book.)

An individual Christian or church must fully understand
their personal perspective on homosexuality based on
Scripture, not as a prerequisite for ministry, but for clarity
of purpose and goals for all involved in this ministry.

Ministry to homosexuals with AIDS—like that to IV-drug
users and teens—often will eventually lead to ministry to
family members and friends of those infected.

Families and Friends
AIDS is becoming more and more a family problem. Not
only do we see parents confronting their sons' homosexuality when AIDS appears, but we are seeing wives infected
by unfaithful or bisexual husbands, and teens infected
through sexually active lifestyles.

No matter what the source of infection in a family, everyone affected needs support. This support takes many
forms: emotional, financial, physical, and spiritual. It can
be relational, such as listening to an individual's anger,
frustration, and fear about death; or practical, such as
picking up someone's groceries or baby-sitting his or her
children. There is a limitless range of ministry to families
affected by the epidemic.

Specific ideas for ministry to those affected by the epidemic include:

ACCEPTANCE. Treat those infected and their families as
you would anyone else. Sit beside them in church, invite
them to your home for dinner, greet them with a hug or a
handshake. Be an example to others through your actions
and reactions, conveying that these are individuals to be
welcomed and loved.

RECONCILIATION. Often families are splintered and
alienated from one another in today's society. A diagnosis
of HIV infection only accentuates that problem. A great
deal can be accomplished toward reconciliation by providing a listening ear. Once you understand all the dynamics
and feelings involved, it may be possible for you to help
put estranged family members into contact again or to help
find a trained counselor to assist in the healing process.

PRACTICAL SUPPORT. As infected individuals progress in their disease, they need increasing assistance in day-to-day activities. Some of the chores others can assist with are: picking up medicine or running errands; laundry and cleaning; trips to the doctor, barber, or hairdresser; trips to church or to visit family members; baby-sitting during work or appointments; providing nutritious meals; help with paying bills or writing letters; making available an extra bedroom for someone with AIDS to live in.

Practical support for families with an infected member can also include: baby-sitting during trips to the hospital to visit the infected relative; providing meals during times of particular stress; opening your home to those coming to your community to visit infected relatives being treated at a local medical facility.

Moreover, you can assist infected individuals and their families with future planning regarding health care, legal issues, and funeral needs. Do let them know you are praying for them all.

SOCIAL SERVICES/NETWORKING. Survey the support services your community and local public health department have to offer PWAs. Medicare, Medicaid, foster care, Social Security, workmen's compensation, health and life insurance coverage, and related legal questions are often a morass of red tape, presenting huge obstacles to the infected individual's ability to deal with the disease. Learning the system will enable you to help others walk through it without becoming overwhelmed. In addition to government programs, local organizations and churches may offer services such as hot meals, child care, and other practical assistance which can augment what you are able to provide.

EMOTIONAL/SPIRITUAL SUPPORT. Besides practical needs, those infected and their families need emotional support as they deal with a long-term, devastating illness. Support groups for people with AIDS and their families can meet great needs.

Everyone affected by this epidemic will need assistance working through grief and spiritual acceptance of circumstances. The strongest of Christians may falter when faced with the reality of a loved one's untimely death. If you or your church are not prepared to offer this support, the AIDS ministries listed in this book can put you in touch with someone in your area who has also dealt with the disease.

Other ways to lend emotional and spiritual support:

☐ Visit regularly both the infected individual and his or her family.

☐ Plan outings which will get them away from the reality of AIDS for a while and offer a fresh perspective.

☐ Take an interest in the illness. Learn about treatments and be able to discuss them intelligently. This will assure your friends that you really care about them and don't simply see them as "ministry opportunities."

☐ Send encouraging notes, cards, balloons, flowers, or posters to brighten a hospital room.

☐ Learn your friends' interests and provide reading materials on the subjects.

☐ Telephone regularly to give an encouraging word. Even those who are themselves shut-ins or without transportation can perform this ministry.

☐ Pray *for* your friends regularly and *with* them whenever possible.

☐ If appropriate, offer to share Bible study with them as they request it.

☐ Provide occasional inspirational music, sermons, or books which might offer encouragement.

As you become more and more involved with PWAs and their families, you will find unending ways to offer the kinds of support which will help them continue in their battle with AIDS.

Care-givers

HIV infection and AIDS devastate both those they infect and those they affect. Health-care professionals and others who regularly work with the infected and their families are also in need of regular support. These workers daily face death and suffering, are depended on for advice and support, and need to continually have their own resources replenished. An effective ministry of support for these care-givers would incorporate emotional and spiritual support ideas similar to those listed above for families.

CORPORATE MINISTRY

The discussion of individuals affected by the epidemic who need ministry provides an overview of the breadth of needs generated by AIDS/HIV, as well as ways that individuals can become involved. What's more, there are several ideas for local churches or Christian organizations who want to become active in AIDS-related ministry. They can:

☐ Research housing opportunities for HIV-positive persons in your area. If no homes or individuals accept AIDS cases, find out what it would take to open a hospice especially for such individuals.

☐ Provide counseling and support for those who feel they may be at risk for infection. These might include those who formerly used IV drugs, engaged in homosexual activity, or were heterosexually promiscuous; Christian women married to unchurched men whose extramarital activity may put them at risk; and teens who have experimented with drugs or sex. Often these people are not infected, but need a place where they can voice their fears and find practical, helpful advice.

☐ Set up an AIDS/HIV crisis line in large metropolitan areas manned by volunteers around the clock for individuals in your community who are infected, their friends, and family members.

☐ Cooperate with other ministries in AIDS-related activity. In Maryland, for example, local churches worked with Prison Fellowship to paint and furnish a new prison wing for inmates with AIDS.

☐ Provide funeral assistance for those who die of AIDS-related diseases. Sometimes, their families have difficulty finding facilities which will perform funeral services.

☐ Organize children and teens to plan a special activity to raise funds for a local or national AIDS ministry: bikeathon, walkathon, talent show, art show, theater production, car wash, pancake breakfast, and so on.

☐ Organize a drive to collect supplies needed by a local hospice or children's home serving PWAs.

SENSITIVE CARING

No matter what form your AIDS-related ministry takes, here are some general thoughts which may assist you in your efforts to be sensitive and caring.

☐ Remember that each individual affected by this disease is a person: a person who used IV drugs, a person who engaged in homosexual behavior, a person who was sexually promiscuous, a person who received a contaminated blood transfusion. By focusing on the person rather than how the virus was acquired, you can avoid boxing people into categories with loaded language and will promote an attitude more in keeping with Christ's.

At the same time, we should stay away from the use of the word "victims" in referring to PWAs. We Christians tend to say children and people with hemophilia are "innocent victims," implying that all others are "guilty victims." Those with AIDS are very sensitive to this language; they gauge your approach to the epidemic in general and to them as individuals by these verbal indicators.

☐ Be very sensitive to the confidentiality surrounding the epidemic at this time. Because of grave concerns over discrimination at the beginning of the epidemic, many state laws are strict regarding the confidentiality of persons with AIDS. Because the church is the body of Christ, we believe that the ideal is an atmosphere where needs and concerns can be shared openly. However, be very cautious that you not divulge information about a person with AIDS without his or her permission.

Some church pastors have dealt with the issue single-handedly because the infected individuals did not want anyone else to know. Other times, a few trusted friends have been involved in ministry to those infected, as well as their families. As the epidemic spreads and the disease becomes a more common occurrence, this atmosphere will undoubtedly change.

In the meantime, be sensitive to the concerns of those to whom you are ministering. At ASAP, we always ask individuals if they are comfortable with us (Shepherd and Anita) discussing their concerns together as husband and wife, or among other staff members. If they are, we work on their situation together. If not, we are most careful not to break their trust.

A key to this issue is creating an atmosphere in your Christian life and your church in which everyone knows he or she is loved and accepted regardless of the sin or problem. Ideally, every church should exude this unconditional love in a way that would draw persons to them for acceptance and healing.

☐ Another key point in this ministry is to remember that through Jesus Christ we offer hope to those in need. Rather than focusing on the chronic illness and death which will ultimately come with the disease, our perspective must be one of hope and eternal life. Cindi Romine, associate pastor of Foursquare Church in San Francisco says, "We do not have all of the answers about healing and death, but we do have the answers about eternity." She suggests the following areas of hope we have to offer people with AIDS: hope for heaven, hope for extended life, hope for forgiveness, hope for healing, and hope for a change of lifestyle.[5]

Tenth Presbyterian Church in Philadelphia started an AIDS ministry called HOPE. The Reverend Ken Larter, HOPE director, has dealt with a range of people infected with HIV, from homeless individuals to Christian professional persons. They receive physical, practical, and spiritual support from HOPE provided by Reverend Larter and the members of the church. Says Larter, "[There is] an ever-increasing need for this kind of ministry as more evangelicals are being touched by [AIDS] and others are seeking peace with God."

HOPE offers everyone who seeks assistance the same promise God made to Hosea in the Old Testament, "I will make the Valley of Achor ["trouble"] a door of hope" (Hosea 2:15).

AIDS AND
THE FAMILY

CHAPTER EIGHT

Family Life in America Today

Few would argue the fact that the American family has changed in our lifetime. The '80s spawned a mountain of studies and books written in an effort to evaluate the effect of the '60s and '70s on the family and to determine where it was heading. We witnessed the emergence of yuppies, crack cocaine, and homeless families. We were concerned as we read about dropping SAT scores and rising illiteracy, and wrung our hands as the teen suicide rate rose to become the second leading cause of death for adolescents.

Though all the experts do not agree on how the nuances and subtleties of the trends impacted the family, some basic factors are indisputable.

FAMILY PROFILE

We hear a lot about the "traditional family." Its virtues are extolled by some, its passing mourned by others. Many hail it as the cornerstone of a strong, moral, and energetic nation. The traditional family unit consisted of father, mother, and children living together, united through marriage, birth, or adoption.

According to Gary Bauer, president of Family Research Council, a Washington, D.C.-based public policy organization affiliated with Focus on the Family, 57 percent of 91 million American households surveyed in the 1989 annual census were headed by married couples. Another 15 percent consisted of family members living together without the presence of a married couple (mostly single-parent families); and 28 percent of all households are what the census bureau calls "nonfamily" households (mostly single people living alone).[1]

Though the majority of American families at the end of the '80s may physically look the same as the traditional family with father, mother, and children present, below the surface the reality is quite different from the traditional family of a generation past.

☐ The divorce rate in the United States between the '50s and '80s doubled, from 2.5 per thousand to 5.2.[2]

☐ The majority of those who divorce will remarry, though experts estimate that these second marriages have a 60 percent chance of also ending in divorce.[3]

☐ In 1980, nearly 6.1 million children lived with stepfamilies. In 1985, that figure had risen to 6.8 million.[4]

☐ In the '50s, most single-parent households were headed by widows; today, primarily divorcees and unwed mothers.[5]

☐ Between 1970 and 1985, births out of wedlock increased at a faster rate than births to married women.[6]

ECONOMIC REALITIES

"No matter how you count it, progress against poverty stopped in 1968 at the Great Society's inception. What went wrong? The answer seems to lie in the massive breakdown in the U.S. family," wrote *Washington Times* editorialist Warren Brookes. Writing on single-parent poverty, Brookes pointed out that the number of black female-headed families between 1960–1985 rose an incredible 26 percent, from 24 percent to 50 percent. Since 1960, the number of white female-headed American families has shot up from 6 percent to 15 percent.[7]

☐ Homeless American families suddenly became visible in the '80s. The gulf between rich and poor families is now wider than at any time since the '40s. The richest 20 percent accounted for 44 percent of the national family income; the poorest 20 percent only got 4.6 percent.[8]

☐ Only the nation's top 20 percent of wage earners increased their share of the nation's income during the '80s, receiving 41.6 percent in 1980 and 44 percent in 1988. The other 80 percent of wage earners saw reductions in their share of the national income between 1980 and 1988 ranging from .3 to .9 percent.[9]

☐ Of the 33 million Americans living below the poverty level, 13 million are children. Five hundred thousand of those children are homeless. By 1987, nearly half of the occupants of the homeless shelters in New York City were children, an average age of six years.[10]

PROFILE OF TEENS

☐ Teen pregnancies rose dramatically from 142,000 in 1950 to a staggering 878,477 in 1986, a growth of 618 percent.[11]

☐ Teen mothers in the '80s were less likely to marry or put their children up for adoption.

☐ Though the overall suicide rate in the United States has risen only slightly since 1950, the teen suicide rate has more than doubled. Now suicide is the second leading cause of death among teens. Among factors that contribute are: changing moral climate, high divorce rate, mobility of society, drug and alcohol abuse, and glorification of violence through media.[12]

☐ Teenage gangs in urban centers have entered the drug trade, using crack cocaine, munitions, and anger.

☐ SAT scores have been dropping since 1955, with only a slight rise in the mid '80s that was not sustained.[13]

☐ American youth have been called passive. For the past 23 years, UCLA's Alexander Astin of the Higher Education Research Institute has been surveying trends in "life goals" of college freshmen. "In the early '70s, the most cherished value was 'developing a meaningful philosophy of life.' By 1989 that value had dropped to ninth, far behind the first choice — 'being well-off financially.' "[14]

According to historian Maris Vinovskis of the University of Michigan, the irony is that we have the best-educated parents in history doing the least for their own children.[15]

POPULATION CHANGES

Like the family, the ethnic mix of the United States is also changing. By 2020, one in three children will come from a minority group — Hispanic-American, African-American, Asian-American, and others. It does not appear that such population shifts will make an improvement in the factors we have just been reviewing, since the breakdown of the traditional family seems to affect all segments of the racial and ethnic mix of our country.

In its study on "Blacks and American Society," the National Research Council of the National Academy of Sciences pointed out that the breakdown of the black family was almost an entirely recent phenomenon: "There was no significant increase in male-absent households even after the massive migrations to the urban North. Until the 1960s, 75 percent of black households with a child under 18 included both husband and wife."[16]

At the same time that the traditional family unit remained more intact in the Hispanic community, Hispanics faced other obstacles intensified by the variety of ethnic groups within their population.

FAITH AND VALUES EVAPORATE

Most disturbing among these alarming trends may be the fact that statistics for American Christian young people were not that different from the overall national pattern. Ross Campbell, M.D., a psychiatrist at the Southeastern Counseling Center in Chattanooga, Tennessee, cites a survey of 8,000 Protestant young people from fifth through ninth grades. Eighty-seven percent of the ninth graders believe that Jesus Christ is the Son of God who died on the cross and rose again. "Unfortunately," he says, "by the time these same young people are eighteen, only twenty percent of them will say they are committed to Christ or will define themselves in any way as Christian. The remaining eighty percent will have lost their faith in the church and the Lord of their parents."[17]

What could wreak such havoc in a society which is the richest in the world, with more natural resources than any other, with an unparalleled history of technology, industry, and science? Dr. Ross has a ready answer: "Family life is deteriorating. Parents are too busy to make special time for their children. Young people are receiving little or no nurturing. Their emotional tanks are empty. They do not feel loved. As a consequence, they are succumbing to negative peer pressure for attention and acceptance.

"It takes a lot out of parents to keep both career and family intact when both of them are working. And far too many parents just don't have the desire or the perseverance. Therefore, something slips, and it is almost always the quality of family life."[18]

In the face of these facts and trends, we need not wonder why our nation is ripe for an epidemic such as HIV infection. In fact, we might wonder why we haven't seen something like this sooner.

In a positive sort of way, though, according to sociologist Arlie Hochschild, we feel uneasy about the future. We are beginning to admit that trading in old-fashioned family values for independence and self-expression has proven much too costly.[19]

The Connecticut Mutual Life Report on American Values in the '80s showed that one factor consistently and dramatically affects the values and behavior of Americans: the level of religious commitment. "Approximately three out of every four U.S. citizens describe themselves as religious and say that religion would become a more important factor in their lives if they knew they had only six months to live. Our findings suggest that the increasing impact of religion on our social and political institutions may be only the beginning of a trend that could change the face of America."[20]

The study goes on to say that in the '80s, religious commitment was a stronger determinant of individual values than whether one was rich or poor, young or old, male or female, black or white, liberal or conservative. This influence of religious beliefs pervades activities in the home, the community, and the workplace, as well as attitudes on social and political issues.

Christian parents and the church ultimately hold the key for turning these disturbing trends around. In his book *Values Begin at Home*, Ted Ward enumerates the values that we learn in the family experience:

☐ Family stability (love, respect, dependability)

☐ Sobriety (importance of taking certain things calmly and seriously)

☐ Frugality (awareness of the importance of conserving rather than wasting)

☐ Community responsibility (concern for one's place as a partner in a social group, in the family, in play, in public settings; cooperativeness, orderliness, and respect)

☐ Concern for learning (valuing the proper uses of curiosity to find out things and to enjoy new awareness)

☐ Concern for ecology (respect for the interrelatedness of things around us)[21]

"The traditional family is dying of neglect and disinterest," Ward says. Referring to the statistics on mothers working outside the home, and on divorce and remarriage, he points to the critical values that should distinguish the Christian family. "Regardless of the particular structure of the family, three basics exist: love, fidelity (between marriage partners), and responsibility (especially for the loving nurture of the children). . . . We should respect the different ways important principles are fulfilled. We should not have major arguments over anything less than the basic principles. In matters of family, let's concentrate on the moral principles of love, fidelity, and responsibility. Through these, the family is a value."[22]

In the same vein, Dr. Ross Campbell agrees that the key to a successful family is more a parental focus on the right things for the child than whether the family has two parents. "Some of the real worries about the breakdown of families are solved by the time we invest in each other," he says. "Commitment to Christian family structure is based on the idea that we love each other. It hinges on the fact that we care about the emotional, physical, psychological, and spiritual needs of all family members."[23]

In the end, what we're yearning for is the quality of life—the values—personified in the traditional family of the '50s. In our longing for better days, we want to believe that life at that time was not as complicated, not as pressure-filled. In some ways, we are right. Children were more protected and did not have as many temptations as early in life 35 years ago. But that generation had its own set of pressures and constraints.

We can yearn to return to traditional values and family, instill that desire in our own children, and nothing will change. Until we stop yearning for that ideal and start pursuing it, we are only part of the problem which needs a solution.

As America searched for an answer to end the AIDS epidemic, it was influenced by the "me" philosophies of the '70s and '80s. Personal responsibility was not emphasized because it might violate the personal rights to privacy and confidentiality, which to many superceded any rights of society or community or family.

In this environment, the family has been ignored as a possible answer. Condoms and free needles are heralded as the way out. The quick-fix approach has allowed individuals to avoid the issue of personal responsibility (except to themselves) and kept them from having to face the messy issue of behavioral change or responsibility to society.

This all occurred at a time when the family faced its greatest trials in America—and yet offered the greatest hope for resolving the AIDS/HIV epidemic. Individual Christians and the local church can impact the nation's response to the epidemic by not falling into the trap of the quick fix.

The decade of the '90s offers us hope through returning to the family and the values it offers. Abstinence until marriage and fidelity in marriage are both the Christian standard and the optimal medical answer. The family offers complete protection which neither condoms nor free needles promise. No longer do we need to send young people mixed messages about sexual responsibility and pleasure.

"The last three decades of drug and sexual experimentation have resulted in great personal tragedy and the erosion of the family," says Dr. Gary Bauer. "History should have taught us that the weakening of the family is the precursor of the breakdown of society. It is little wonder that AIDS and HIV spread so quickly across America. Yet, hope rests in the reestablishment of the traditional Judeo-Christian family unit. Many of societal ills, including AIDS, will virtually disappear when the goal of family rises above the goal of personal gratification alone."

CHAPTER NINE
Risk-producing Behaviors

Amid the myriad of activities practiced in our nation today, scientists have been able to identify the two that account for nearly all HIV infection. While some AIDS cases we see today are also attributed to infected blood and perinatal transmission (infected mother to infant), the original infection in the blood donor or in the mother is nearly always traceable to one of the two risk behaviors already discussed: having multiple sexual partners or sharing IV-drug paraphernalia.

Interestingly, when hearing this, many Christians still feel insulated from the virus in the belief that Christians do not engage in these activities. One pastor in the Midwest made the pious claim, "People in my church don't get AIDS because we don't do that kind of thing." Either that congregation is unlike most in the nation or that pastor doesn't know his parishioners very well — or doesn't want to admit what he knows.

But a growing number of leaders, like James Dobson and Josh McDowell, are challenging us Christians to confront ourselves and our weaknesses honestly; and are giving us the tools to change patterns and behaviors in an effort to reach the biblical standard God has provided for us.

In looking at the two behaviors that put people at greatest risk for contracting HIV infection (particularly sexual contact with multiple partners), let us objectively admit they are prevalent in society and that they are also present in the Christian community. Let's face our responsibilities not only in terms of upholding biblical standards of behavior, but in literally saving others' lives by helping them understand the risks involved if they fail to heed the warnings.

DRUG USE

Signs and statistics of increased drug abuse surround us. Since the stigma has been lessened for those in the public eye to admit their addictions, we have seen a steady stream of entertainers, politicians, and celebrities entering treatment for one form of substance abuse or another. The positive side of this trend is that it has definitely brought the problem into the open and made it more a mainstream issue. The negative side is that we have been forced to realize how widespread and far-reaching the problem of addictions is in our nation. The struggle of public figures with addictions mirrors the plight of the general population.

Enrollment in the federal government's assistance program for employees seeking help for drug abuse rose 18 percent in a 12-month period between 1987 and 1988.[1] Dr. David Musto, a medical historian, calls addiction "the American disease." A *Newsweek* report on addiction observed: "Other nations surely suffer. But this country appears to have been rendered especially vulnerable to the drug scourge—on one hand, by careering, fast-lane affluence that denies itself no thrill that can be bought; and on the other by a racial and economic divisiveness that has made social alienation a way of life in the ghettos. A generation ago heroin took a dreadful toll on the minority poor. Nowadays, high-priced cocaine and its nickel-and-dime derivative crack have left their mark at both ends of the social spectrum. And alcohol may be the oldest abused substance of all."[2]

Indeed, the United States is the biggest user of illegal drugs in the industrialized world. With only five percent of the world's population, it consumes 50 percent of the world's annual output of cocaine. Americans create the demand which struggling Third-World countries seek to supply.

Former drug "czar" William Bennett kept the issue before the nation. However, those who live in the Washington, D.C. area need only turn on the evening news to learn daily of the murders of still more drug dealers. Innocent bystanders who happened to get in the way of the drug lords who vie for total control of the city territory are also listed from time to time as casualties.

In general, white American parents don't feel their kids have much of a drug problem but that kids of other races do. However, a study released in late 1989 by the National Parent's Resource Institute for Drug Education (PRIDE) revealed that overall drug and alcohol use was more prevalent among whites than blacks. Approximately 350,000 students in grades 6–12 were surveyed in 38 states and the District of Columbia during the 1988–89 school year.

The survey concluded that the teenager most likely to be an underaged drinker and illegal drug user was a white male; the least likely was a black female. Of the 42,000 seniors surveyed, twice the percentage of whites used hard liquor as blacks, and nearly twice the percentage of whites used marijuana and cocaine as blacks. Three times as many whites used hallucinogenic drugs as blacks.[3]

Most of us will admit the problem in our society at large. But how much has drug use infiltrated the church? Steve Arterburn and Jim Burns, authors of *Drug-Proof Your Kids*, report on a study of the church and substance abuse. "Ninety-two percent of the pastors surveyed said drug abuse is a major problem among young people in their communities. However, when asked if there's a serious problem in their own churches, only thirteen percent said yes. Yet the same study showed only a slight difference between churched and unchurched youth when it comes to usage of drugs and alcohol." The study, done by the Gallup organization, found alcohol usage nearly equal—80 percent for the churched youth versus 88 percent for the unchurched. Surprisingly, 38 percent of unchurched youth had tried marijuana, while considerably more—47 percent—of church youth had. At the same time, 14 percent of unchurched youth had tried cocaine, as had 11 percent of churched youth.[4]

For Christians, recognizing the problem within our communities might be easier if we thought in terms of "drug use" rather than "drug addiction." This is a very legitimate way to examine the problem. The U.S. Department of Health and Human Services' Alcohol, Drug Abuse, and Mental Health Administration points out the four stages of drug use: experimentation; more frequent use; intense pre-occupation and daily use; and finally, increasing levels of the drug needed to maintain normal activities.[5]

To honestly face the issue within the church, we must admit that even stage-one experimentation not only opens the door to drug use itself but also for HIV infection. Though teens who simply experiment with drugs are not at great risk of contracting HIV through that route (since most who experiment would not use IV methods), all AIDS experts and researchers agree that alcohol and drug use enhance one's chance of contacting the virus. Why? The substances reduce inhibitions and increase the possibility that an individual will participate in sexual behavior either in exchange for drugs or under their influence; hence, the risk for contracting the virus.

SEXUAL ACTIVITY

While we all realize drugs are a scourge on this generation of Americans, we likewise recognize the high level of sexual activity that occurs. One needs only to look at the following data to understand the magnitude of the problem.

☐ Sexually transmitted diseases (other than HIV) are on the rise in the U.S. For example, CDC reported 40,275 cases of primary and secondary syphilis for 1987, up 47 percent from 27,273 cases in 1986.[6]

☐ Each year, more than one million teens will become pregnant, four out of five of them will be unmarried, and some 30,000 under age 15. If this trend continues, a full 40 percent of today's 14-year-old girls will be pregnant at least once before the age of 20.[7]

☐ Nearly half of black females become pregnant by age 20. The pregnancy rate among ages 15–19 is almost twice that among whites. Ninety percent of the babies born to blacks in this age-group are born out of wedlock and most are reared in fatherless homes.[8]

☐   According to a 1986 Harris poll, 57 percent of adolescent boys and girls had sex before age 18. By the time
they reached their mid-20s, many no longer regarded sexual relationships as a matter of values or commitment.[9]

Dr. Lillian Rubin of the Institute for the Study of Social
Change at the University of California at Berkeley says that
her research indicates a shift in behavior standards in the
last decade to a point where teenagers have developed a
widely held sense that they are entitled to have sex. Rubin
says the trend appears to cut across economic and geographic lines.

"I've conducted 300 face-to-face, in-depth interviews
with kids across the country and mailed out 600 question-
naires," Rubin said. "I've found it doesn't make any difference whether the kids live in a big city or a small town."

One of the teens interviewed commented, "A lot of my
friends feel that everybody's using the AIDS thing to scare
kids into not having sex. It's not going to work. I don't
know of one person my age who's dead of AIDS."[10]

Are these statistics different among churched youth?
Josh McDowell surveyed teenagers in eight evangelical denominations to find out. Of the respondents, 82 percent
stated that they attended church each week; 79 percent
stated they were actively involved in their churchs' youth
programs; and 82 percent said they knew Jesus Christ as
their personal Saviour.

On evaluating the survey responses, McDowell found
that by age 18, 43 percent of these churched youth had
experienced intercourse; and 65 percent had engaged in
fondling breasts or genitals and/or had sexual intercourse;
by age 13, 20 percent of the youth had engaged in fondling
activity and, by age 16, 53 percent. Thirty-six percent were
not able to state that sexual intercourse before marriage
was unacceptable, and 55 percent could not state that they
believed fondling breasts was morally unacceptable behavior before marriage.

Nearly three of ten (26 percent) of these churched youth
said they would be more likely to have intercourse if they
were positive pregnancy would not result. Twenty-eight
percent said they would be more likely to have intercourse
if their parents would not find out. And 22 percent of
churched youth would become sexually active if their par-

ents would not object. Nearly four out of ten (39 percent) claimed that intercourse would be acceptable if they intended to marry their partners.

Given a list of ten primary sources for information about sex and sexual relations, the teens surveyed rated the sources in order from most frequent resource to least: friends, movies, parents, television, school classes, books, the Bible, "adult" movies, brothers/sisters, and the church.

In describing their emotional situations, the teens surveyed felt they were misunderstood (49 percent), lonely (38 percent), and discouraged (39 percent). The weaker the teens' relationships with their parents, the greater their chances of feeling lonely or discouraged. Females were more likely than males to suffer from loneliness.[11]

Does sexual behavior change once churched youth reach college? The Josh McDowell findings were borne out by a Gallup survey of college students done for the Christian Broadcasting Network. Students from 100 U.S. colleges were surveyed, 99 percent of them unmarried. Though only 52 percent of the evangelicals believed premarital sex is wrong, 28 percent acknowledged having sex regularly; 30 percent reported having had more than one sexual partner.[12]

These grim statistics force us to admit that the young people in our churches practice sexual behavior not unlike society at large. Though we did not find good data on churched adult sexual behavior, we can make some assumptions based on the infidelity and divorce rates we have personally observed within the church.

Are people in the evangelical church at risk for HIV and AIDS? Sadly, looking at the data, we must respond with an unequivocal yes.

Benjamin Franklin said, "Sin is not hurtful because it is forbidden, but it is forbidden because it is hurtful." American Christians seem to have had difficulty embracing this truth when it comes to sexual activity and drug use. Based on the studied behavior, we can say that the Scriptures have apparently not convinced us of this truth. Sermons have not convinced us of this truth. Threats and venereal disease have not convinced us of this truth. Unfortunately, it might take life-threatening AIDS to force us to stop short and evaluate behavior, lifestyle, and attitudes in light of Scripture.

Churchgoers can no longer attend church on Sundays and only give lip service to the behaviors Christians are expected to model the rest of the week. The actions of many in the church show that they believe experimenting with drugs or sex or having that brief extramarital affair are not harmful, even though forbidden. Indeed, these actions are forbidden because they are hurtful—spiritually, emotionally, relationally, and physically harmful. More than that, these behaviors may literally kill us and those we love.

In regard to HIV infection, we must remember two things. First, it is not who we are but what we do that puts us at risk for acquiring this disease. Second, we must be very careful not to think of AIDS/HIV in the context of "us" and "them." Anyone—even you—can become infected if exposed intimately to someone else who is.

Knowledge as well as behavior must direct us in controlling AIDS. Someone who remains abstinent until marriage may marry someone who hasn't. Until all remain abstinent, people must know the HIV status of their sexual partners—even entering a first marriage (and for some, even within the marriage).

We cannot wait. Most of the AIDS epidemic of the '90s has already been determined by the HIV infections of the '80s. If we want to save ourselves and the next generation from spiritual and physical devastation, the time to act is now.

CHAPTER TEN
Prevention as Protection

AIDS activists, politicians, and public health officials have said over and over that education is our only weapon against HIV infection and AIDS since there is no cure or vaccine. Until that time, they argue, individuals need to be made aware of the dangers of HIV infection, assuming that such awareness will result in behavioral changes. These changes in behavior, combined with the use of condoms, constitute what has been termed "safe sex" or "safer sex."

We will discuss in this chapter not only safe and safer sex practices, but also "safest sex" practices as well. We will also evaluate whether education really is the only weapon we have against the virus and whether the commonly shared AIDS wisdom of today is, in fact, wise or not. Finally, we will look at how the church can play a critical role in stopping the spread of this epidemic through its influence on young Americans.

Having grown up in a medical family with a father who had both a medical and public health degree, I (Shepherd) can remember as a youngster in the early '50s the excitement my father shared about preventative medicine techniques and the value of early diagnosis. In fact, I can even recall his attending specific events in the early to mid '50s from which he would return nearly ecstatic about how medicine would be able to intervene in the earliest stages of many diseases and prevent them from progressing.

ASAP believes that traditional medical practices should

be applied to HIV infection and that there are specific values in the knowledge of infection. However, the conventional wisdom today which has dictated the course of our nation's response to this epidemic has contended that general education about this disease is all we are able to give individuals and the public to affect the course, speed, and force of the spread of AIDS.

IS EDUCATION ALONE ENOUGH?

One report released at the end of 1989 by the Citizens Committee on AIDS of Northern New Jersey and New York, criticized national AIDS education efforts as being ineffective in stopping the epidemic's spread. "Despite many excellent and innovative programs," the report says, "prevention and education efforts in general have been underfunded, erratic, uncoordinated, confusing, and timid. The results have been correspondingly meager. Many people engaging in high-risk behaviors do not understand or acknowledge their risk and have not changed behavior."

The report went on to say that, just as we have no therapeutic "magic bullet" for AIDS, there is no educational panacea. "Prevention is a complex problem that calls for changes in deeply rooted attitudes and behavior by individuals, partners in sexual and drug-using relationships, and by society in general."[1]

We would argue that while general education certainly does heighten awareness, it does not effectively interrupt the chain of viral transmission through significant behavior change. That is accomplished through specific knowledge of infection and traditional public health intervention strategies, such as confidential reporting and partner notification. When the data on individuals who have gone for testing and found they were positive is evaluated, we learn that only about 10 percent of the total number of estimated people infected know their HIV-seropositive status.

That means, then, that a full 90 percent of people who are believed infected in America today do not know they are and, as a result, are unintentionally and unknowingly infecting others. Our public health community, driven by many AIDS activists and experts, could probably not have devised a better way of driving this epidemic underground than the programs in place at the end of the '80s.

How did we arrive at this state of affairs? Why don't more people know their HIV status? Why have we argued that education alone is the only weapon in our arsenal? Why has ignorance of infection rather than knowledge of infection dictated our response?

The reason probably relates back to a fundamental belief mistakenly held since the beginning that the epidemic was, in fact, a homosexual disease and not one that would spread to other communities. Consequently, the gay community dictated policy for some time. A great many of their lifestyle patterns involved having multiple sexual partners (in some instances as many as 40 to 100 a month). Rather than focusing on monogamous sexual relationships or none at all, a strategy was devised which would allow multiple-partner relationships to continue while reducing risk of exposure to the virus.

This concept of risk reduction or risk elimination was originally called "safe sex." Safe sex, when first promoted included (among other things), normal, unprotected sexual intercourse with a woman for heterosexuals, since it was believed that women would not contract this virus. For homosexuals, the strategy to maintain multiple relations and yet be protected was based on the use of spermicides and condoms. The original term "safe" was changed to "safer" when it was discovered that spermicides and condoms did not offer complete protection from infection.

Two significant studies gave us preliminary data on the degree of risk individuals faced when using condoms exclusively in a relationship. The first by Dr. Margaret Fischl involved heterosexual couples in which one of the partners already had symptomatic AIDS. Those couples which abstained from sex but otherwise shared the same facilities in an intimate home setting had zero conversions to HIV. Couples who exclusively used condoms showed a 17-percent seroconversion rate over a 12–18-month period. Finally, in couples using no barrier protection (condoms), 81 percent of the uninfected partners contracted HIV from their spouses over the same period.[2]

The second study, conducted by the federal government in the Los Angeles area, was ultimately withdrawn in

August 1988 because participants were placed at too great a risk of contracting the virus. In this $2.6-million study, the government enrolled homosexual men and followed those who used condoms exclusively. Because there was such a dramatic occurrence of breakage or improper use resulting in exposure to infected-partner body fluids, the study was hastily terminated. Two months later, Surgeon General Koop endorsed the Ad Council's public service ad campaign which focused nearly exclusively on the use of condoms to protect individuals from HIV infection.

So, "safe sex" became "safer sex," but the issue of "safest sex" was barely discussed. Proponents of abstinence immediately lost their credibility in discussions of AIDS education among AIDS activists. However, the optimal medical message with no moral overtones is for individuals to avoid exposure to the virus. Since we know exposure occurs when an uninfected individual comes into intimate sexual or IV contact with an infected individual, then the concept of abstinence from a medical perspective unquestionably must be promoted. Amazingly, few in the medical community have had the courage to speak out forcefully on behalf of abstinence.

Dr. Robert R. Redfield is one notable exception. He courageously shares with all audiences the need to promote sexual responsibility. The irony of Dr. Koop's strong endorsement of condoms is that he had spoken out earlier against other behaviors which potentially jeopardize people's health and sometimes result in death. The message Koop gave regarding smoking, for example, was "Don't smoke," not "Use low-tar or filter cigarettes." And he said this knowing full well that many millions of Americans would continue to smoke; still the optimal medical message was "Don't." This message of avoidance or abstinence that the public health service sent and continues to send is consistent with all behavioral activities that result in negative consequences, with the exception of sex.

The challenge, then, to the church is not only to be able to send messages which are effective within the church, but also to affect the entire development of appropriate messages to the general population regarding "safest sex" practices. These messages are given on the air, they are espoused in schools, and are certainly the gist of most

AIDS publications. They need to be in the best interest of our young people; they need to be honest and consistent. If condoms fail and result in HIV infection a significant percentage of the time, then the sexually active to whom we recommend the use of condoms need to understand what risks they take. We must educate in a way that saves lives, not jeopardizes them. And we must begin by working from a position of knowledge of infection. We must encourage people to learn their HIV status so that they can, if positive, receive optimal medical care, plan their futures, and not infect those they love.

THE OPTIMAL PREVENTION MESSAGE

Education for young people can play a significant role in affecting the course of the epidemic. But that education must assist them in decision-making; give them direction, understanding, and purpose; and convey that we have their best interests in mind, or else our messages about AIDS/HIV will be ineffective.

The starting point, therefore, is to ask ourselves, "What is the optimal message?" and "Is it realistic in this day and age to convey messages to young people that focus on delaying sexual activity until marriage and then remaining faithful in marriage?"

"Our youth are too precious to lose to a voluntary epidemic," says Peggy Markell, R.N., founder of the Massena Natural Family Planning Center and former cochair of the AIDS Education Committee of the St. Lawrence County Chapter of the American Red Cross. "We as a society have a great deal to lose when we consider that approximately 88 percent of the AIDS cases are in the range of ages 20 to 49 years old."

Mrs. Markell believes that the mixed messages sent through AIDS education efforts have contributed to the apathy among teens and the belief that they are not at risk for infection. Speaking to pastors and church leaders at the National Conference on HIV '89, she said, "Most of our teens are still in the experimental stage of their drug use and sexual activity. It is the easiest time to change the behavior given the proper skills and good support.

"The push for condoms in AIDS education makes an unfair assumption that our young people are incapable of self-control. This is disrespectful, defeatist, and discriminatory. We are not even giving these kids a chance. We're giving up on them before we allow them an opportunity to try to make a difference in their lives."

A family life educator, Mrs. Markell promotes chastity education which concentrates on the whole person: learning to become a loving person, the proper role of sex in life, and respecting and protecting our own dignity.

"Kids today find it easier to take off their clothes and share their bodies than to take off their masks and share their hopes and dreams," she says. "We need to instead help teens understand how to develop healthy relationships based on respect, caring, and affection."

Again, the reality of the environment in which young Americans are growing up today argues not only for teaching proper behavior, but also for teaching refusal skills which will allow young people to overcome peer pressures to participate in either sexual or drug activities. The messages cannot be "Just say no." We want to give ways for saying no, such as, "No, not yet," "Not now," "Not you," or "Not ever." And we must go far beyond clever responses to give fundamental reasons, values, and rewards for sexual responsibility.

It is important to address the issue of condoms since they certainly are the one solution offered by many teachers and are prominently displayed on the counters of most drug stores in America. We must explain that those who do participate in sexual activity using condoms should be prepared for the possibility of becoming infected over time. Condoms reduce the risk of HIV infection but they do not eliminate it.

Significant risk accompanies condom use. The Los Angeles study cited before indicated that improper use or breakage occurred as often as 50 percent of the time; Fischl's study concluded a 17-percent seroconversion rate. Even a one- to five-percent failure rate—when death in all probability will result—is extremely significant. If we share this information in that context, we will have fulfilled our obligation in teaching what is best and fully in other people's interest.

The notions of confidentiality and right to privacy heavily influence the discussion of proper educational messages. Arguments have been made that if an individual has the ability to retain total confidentiality about his or her positive HIV status, then there is no need for anyone to know. But the benefits of one knowing that he or she is infected are negated. We must always stress that the value of knowledge is for personal benefit and not public notice. However, there is more benefit to infected persons if certain other people know than if they don't know.

Another aspect of AIDS education in the schools which the church finds very sensitive is that the schools not only teach about the transmission of HIV but about many sexual practices which go beyond the traditional male-female relationship. True, young people need to understand that different practices occur so they can avoid certain behaviors; still, it is also important not to put into their minds particular sexual acts or relationships which they might not otherwise have considered.

Scripture teaches sexual responsibility, and Ephesians 5 gives directions on how we can do this responsibly. Not only must we take care to portray what is proper conduct, but we are directed not even to mention to young people those activities which God abhors (v. 12). This is consistent with Genesis 3:22, where God shows great concern over anyone who gains the knowledge of evil being able to eat of the tree of life and live forever, as if living eternally with the knowledge of evil would be the worst possible life.

Sex is truly a gift from God but like any gift, it can be and has been abused by many. We have been shocked to learn of some of the deviant sexual practices among certain lifestyles which we feel have no value and are in no way pleasing to God. The idea that sex alone is an end in itself is one of the fundamental mistakes which allowed this epidemic to initially spread so rapidly. Sex in the Christian context involves not just an act but relationship, responsibility, feelings and emotions, and a spiritual dimension. Sex, therefore, involves the body, mind, and soul and needs to be discussed holistically. The challenge will be to change the thought process of young people regarding sexual activity in order to form the basis for actual behavioral change.

PREVENTION THROUGH BEHAVIORAL CHANGE

The church has historically been the glue to hold society together through the bonding of the family. Christ's teachings offer hope to America and to the world as they face this terrible epidemic. The modern church is beginning to provide answers for people in need.

Scripture shows clearly how individuals should conduct their sexual and interpersonal relationships. Unfortunately, men and women have the ability to rationalize nearly any behavior contrary to Scripture. David certainly was able to send Uriah into the front lines of battle to gain Uriah's wife Bathsheba. Other examples, such as Lot and the Corinthian church (1 Cor. 5), evidence that believers can veer from godly living. We probably all know someone in everyday life who has crossed the line into sexual temptations. Certainly, we are all familiar with personal struggles.

The sexual revolution of the '60s and '70s created the hotbed in which the HIV virus would eventually flourish. It was a failed revolution and the seeds that were sown by it are now being harvested in death and destruction. Nevertheless, the underlying behaviors which allow the virus to be transmitted are ultimately what must change in order to limit the spread of the HIV epidemic.

Having more than one lifetime sexual partner now involves considerable risk. Homosexuals, who in large measure have shaped America's response to AIDS to date, experienced high rates of infection until, as a group, their number of sexual partners was curtailed. This lesson should be learned quickly before the virus becomes well established in the rest of the American population.

A 1988 study done by Greenwich House, a drug rehabilitation facility in New York City, revealed that an overwhelming majority of participants in this program (namely, hard-core IV-drug users) felt there was either a very slight chance or no chance at all that they would ever become HIV positive. However, when the individuals in the study were tested for HIV, more than one third tested positive.

This is denial in its essence. The reasons that the individuals in the Greenwich study gave for not being tested were equally remarkable, considering the fact that we have established a system of voluntary testing. Two thirds of those responding stated that they either did not feel they had been exposed to the virus or simply did not want to know. Only nine percent had concerns about confidentiality (the factor guiding most AIDS legislation in the 1980s).[3]

In the same study, which was conducted over a three-month period, AIDS education seemed to have relatively little impact on behavioral patterns. So what does it take to change behaviors? How do we reach individuals to protect them from this dread disease?

The first part of any behavioral change program is to establish among young people correct behaviors that don't require change. Changing established patterns, even in the face of a fatal disease, is proving to be very difficult. We must reach the young of America before they begin multiple-partner sexual contact or IV-drug activity, and so establish harmful patterns that will be hard to change later.

Some programs are seeing excellent and encouraging results. One such curriculum is Sex Respect, directed by Kathleen Sullivan in Golf, Illinois. The program objectives include: improving awareness and recognition of potentially harmful consequences of early sexual activity; increasing adherence to attitudes and values supporting abstinence from sexual relations among teenagers; increasing willingness and motivation of teens to delay or avoid early sexual activity; to improve skills which help teens resist pressure to be sexually involved; to increase moral and social support from peers, family, and community for teens who refrain from sexual activity; to help create counter-peer pressure on behalf of self-restraint; to infuse health education programs for adolescents with greater emphasis on saying no to potentially harmful behaviors; to broadly disseminate information promoting sexual self-restraint; and to increase parental involvement and the level of interaction between parents and teens concerning the value of abstinence and sexual self-restraint.

An evaluation of program effectiveness done late in 1989 revealed that abstinence is well received among today's adolescents. Before the program was instituted in the schools which now use the curriculum, 34 percent of students said there a were "a lot" of benefits to waiting until marriage for sexual intercourse. This increased to 57 percent after the program was instituted. The study showed that the impact is broad-based. Younger and older students, males and females, students living with both parents or in other family arrangements, students with poorly educated or highly educated parents, regular church-attenders and those who seldom or never attend church, and students doing well or poorly in school all showed important changes in the desired direction.

This pattern of results was similar for other items measuring program effects on these attitudes and beliefs. The perceived benefits of "secondary virginity," for example, seemed greater following the program. Before the program, about 42 percent felt that teens who had previously had sex would benefit by stopping sexual activity and waiting until marriage. Afterward, 62 percent held this opinion. Yet, the study also showed that if the message of abstinence is not reinforced regularly, students often revert to previous attitudes and behaviors.

Like appropriate behavior changes, faithfulness within marriage safeguards against the spread of AIDS. We met a young woman whose father was not faithful to his wife. In fact, he had sexual relationships outside of marriage with other men. He became HIV positive and unfortunately infected his wife.

This man was a prominent member of his community and church and yet had a sexual addiction that his family was totally unaware of. The sad part of this story is that, while he knew he was HIV positive, he did not inform his wife, even when he became chronically ill. On reflection, it should not surprise us that people who are unfaithful do not have enough concern and respect for their spouses to inform them of the physical threat they pose.

The wife was totally unaware of her own HIV status when she offered to be present when her daughter gave birth to her first grandchild. The doctor predicted a complicated delivery and the mother specifically came to be available to donate blood during delivery. This story could have ended tragically with the destruction of not just one generation, but three. As it turned out, the delivery went smoothly without complications and the mother did not have to contribute her blood. Some months later, the mother learned the cause of her husband's many illnesses and shortly after that became ill herself.

THE ROLE OF THE CHURCH
AND THE CHRISTIAN IN PREVENTION

As this story illustrates, besides sending strong prevention messages to young people, the church can also encourage individuals to learn their HIV status if they feel they've been exposed to the virus. An immeasurable benefit to treating an individual who is stricken by AIDS is that he or she will not have infected a loved one. By early knowledge of HIV infection, individuals can stop the cycle of infection. We cannot overstate the importance and value of this knowledge. The United States has approached this epidemic to date largely from the position of ignorance; now it is time we approach it with the power of knowledge.

While serving on a school board's advisory panel on AIDS, I (Shepherd) realized that abstract teaching has very little relevance to young people and certainly is not the way to reach them. The more knowledge of infection we have, the more concrete and effective our educational messages can be. Saying, "Many teenagers in America are now infected with HIV," may not influence the young people you are addressing. But saying, for example, "There are eight infected students in the local high school" (without naming names, of course) will definitely get their attention.

We've also learned that individuals who know they are HIV positive are also much more apt to change their behaviors than those who don't know. By combining what Scripture teaches with specific knowledge, we can change behaviors and limit the spread of this epidemic. However, we cannot afford to wait any longer to begin this process.

The responsibility we have in educating young people about AIDS is very great considering the social pressures today that surround them regarding sex. We must not only give young people examples of proper behavioral patterns, but also sound advice on how to achieve them. Simply saying this or that is what they should do is not enough. We must also offer skills that allow people to attain these goals. Refusal skills are necessary to be able to parry the many advances and temptations made repeatedly over time on our youth from so many different avenues. This equipping cannot be done in a one-time lecture, but must be a continual process.

We must acknowledge that many have already slipped into behavioral patterns that will put them at risk. The Josh McDowell survey cited earlier found that young Christians are sexually active. While their activity may not be as intense as that of non-Christians, it nevertheless is cause for great concern. How do we change life patterns, then, of individuals who are seeking different forms of gratification through sex or drugs?

First, we must establish avenues of communication. This is often difficult for authority figures since conventional wisdom says that authority is not to be trusted. At the same time, many authorities have shown little genuine concern for teens. Establishing a relationship of trust requires a long-term commitment and a full understanding and appreciation of where young people are today.

Next, we need to focus on the benefits of abstinence which lasts until marriage. Those who have already experimented sexually can benefit from secondary virginity, wherein one can make a commitment to remain celibate until marriage, regardless of past history.

Addressing the issue of sexual morality in *Mere Christianity*, C.S. Lewis wrote:

"God knows our situation; He will not judge us as if we had no difficulties to overcome. What matters is the sincerity and perseverance of our will to overcome them. Before we can be cured we must want to be cured. ... We may, indeed, be sure that perfect chastity — like perfect charity — will not be attained by any merely human efforts. You must ask for God's help. Even when you have done so, it may seem to you for a long time that no help, or less help than you need, is being given. Never mind. After each failure ask forgiveness, pick yourself up, and try again. Very often what God first helps us towards is not the virtue itself but just this power of always trying again. For however important chastity ... may be, this process trains us in habits of the soul which are more important still. It cures our illusions about ourselves and teaches us to depend on God. ... The only fatal thing is to sit down content with anything less than perfection."[4]

And finally, we must continually reinforce the value of marriage and fidelity within marriage. Unfortunately, Christian couples are too often torn apart by unfaithfulness. In the age of AIDS, the dangers this presents to the family structure are too great a risk for any caring individuals to accept. The need for examples of fidelity are increasingly urgent and should not be underestimated by any church body entering into a program of teaching sexual responsibility in relationship to AIDS.

As Christian leaders and parents lead pure and undefiled lives, our youth will experience the benefits of godly living and emulate those examples. In this way, the church can give the gift of full and rewarding lives to young people by teaching them behaviors which will keep them from ever having to personally experience the pain of HIV infection.

IV

AIDS AND THE INDIVIDUAL CHRISTIAN

CHAPTER ELEVEN

One Christian's Perspective on Suffering

When Billy Graham went to the Soviet Union for his first evangelistic crusade in 1981, he was heavily criticized for preaching on a passage about obeying those in authority (Rom. 13:1). The press asked on his return how he could make such statements in light of the extensive repression and suffering there among Christians. We felt his response at the time was quite remarkable and profound: "What's wrong with suffering?" he asked.

What *is* wrong with suffering? Dr. Graham pointed out that some of the greatest growth in the church historically has occurred when it was under the greatest repression. To those living the worldly life, suffering has only a negative value; but when extended to the spiritual dimension, it can in fact be of great value to the individual. In James 1:2, we read: "Consider it pure joy, my brothers, whenever you face trials of many kinds." And in Romans 5:1-4, we see what suffering can produce in the end: greater character and hope.

We'll return to these themes of joy, hope, and character, but first let's reflect on what Billy Graham saw and said. Shortly after his trip which, we can see in retrospect, was a significant event in the relaxing of relations between West and East, China began to open its doors even wider. What amazed many Christians, when allowed to return to China, was that the repressed Chinese church had actually grown, though the missionaries had been expelled decades before.

The spiritual seeds that had been planted had been faith-
fully watered and cultivated through the power of the Holy
Spirit.

Dr. Graham also understood the power of God and His
Word working in such an environment. In fact, it now turns
out that a great deal of the movement for democracy and a
greater voice for individuals in many of the Eastern Bloc
countries was cultivated through the church. However,
when Dr. Graham was criticized, not only by the press but
even by some of his own followers, he was able to view
events of the time in a historical perspective that included
a spiritual dimension. Most important, he intimately understood, trusted, and placed his faith in that Spirit and power
of God. Is there a lesson to be learned from this for those
facing the AIDS/HIV epidemic?

The magnitude and diversity of suffering generated by
AIDS is well documented. Today many fears are being lessened through scientific knowledge and experience with
this disease. The fact remains, however, that the premature
death that many will face will have significant impact on
their families, friends, coworkers, and fellow congregation
members. Beyond those immediately affected by the presence of HIV, all of American society will feel the economic
and cultural strain created by the spreading of the epidemic. AIDS/HIV will prove a reason for much sacrifice and
suffering if the United States and the world are to survive
them intact.

In preparation, we as Christians must be faithful to the
Word in light of this terrible epidemic and count it all joy
as we face the considerable trials before us.

WHAT IS SUFFERING?

To be precise, we can divide suffering into four categories:
the suffering of Christ; our suffering persecution as He did
for His sake; sharing the pain of others; and suffering in
ways common to all people in the course of living. As
Christians we find all forms of suffering to be interrelated
because any form — whether physical, mental, or spiritual — can lead to personal growth, particularly in relationship to God.

Suffering, by most definitions, is enduring hardships and feeling pain. The concept of suffering in much of today's prosperous American church seems to have little relevance or to be a wholly spiritual dimension. Whether or not we hold to a prosperity-type theology, most of us live as if our faith were synonymous with the lifestyles to which we have become accustomed. We somehow believe that if we accept Christ into our lives, good things lie in store for us. This is not the message given in Scripture, but rather a cultural influence on Americans in this day and age.

Suffering is often seen as a product of failure to achieve a given goal, failure to succeed in sports, in interpersonal relationships, in school, or on the job. A teacher once said that if you bat .500 in life, you've probably done quite well; that life is a mixture of successes and failures; and that through failures, we can truly learn to succeed.

During a period of personal hardship, I (Shepherd) was given a quote of considerable merit, though attributed to no particular author: "Every day each of us makes decisions which determine the direction our lives will move. No one, no matter how wise or highly principled, can make the right decision every time. To err is no disgrace. Disgrace lies in not learning from our mistakes, not picking ourselves up, brushing ourselves off, and trying again." To fail and to suffer is part of life. From our failures, many of which are excruciatingly painful, we can learn and grow. That is certainly the promise God gives us in growing spiritually closer to Him.

On the other hand, suffering often hits us through no act of our own. Twentieth-century Americans tend to see themselves as "innocent victims" of fate or circumstance. As Christians, we must look at suffering in light of God's Word and intent as well as from the perspective of personal hurt or pain. Whether caused by an individual's failure or mere circumstances, the suffering which results can have a positive outcome and be a significant benefit.

While the AIDS epidemic is a scourge, it is also an opportunity for the church, since many individuals will be facing the reality of death or eternal life. The opportunity for eternal life arises from suffering and to many this will be a great gift. Those who offer help will be rewarded as well by being a part of the growing process.

SUFFERING IN THE CONTEXT OF GOD'S WILL

A search of Scripture for references to suffering reveals an amazing number of New Testament passages portraying it positively. We already mentioned Romans 5:1-4 which reads, "Since we have been justified through faith. . . . we rejoice in the hope of the glory of God. Not only so, but we also rejoice in our sufferings."

Paul often speaks of suffering in his writing, but we read Christ's words in Luke 24:26, "Did not the Christ have to suffer these things and then enter His glory?" In the Old Testament, Isaiah 52–53 predicts that the Messiah would be One who would suffer at the hands of man. Christ fully understood that in order to redeem man He would have to suffer. And that we, like Him, would suffer as well in order to gain eternal life. Luke shares with us in Acts 5:41 that those early followers of Christ rejoiced that they were counted worthy to suffer dishonor in the name of Christ. Worthy to suffer? How many of us truly are willing and ready to suffer for Him or for others? And how many of us who are willing and ready consider suffering an *imprimatur* that we are worthy—or capable—of following our Lord?

In *The Cost of Discipleship*, Dietrich Bonhoeffer addresses the issue of suffering: "The disciple is a disciple only in so far as he shares his Lord's suffering and rejection and crucifixion. . . . If we refuse to take up our cross and submit to suffering and rejection at the hands of men, we forfeit our fellowship with Christ and have ceased to follow Him."[1]

The concept of suffering developed by Paul indicates that we make up one body and, as various members of that body, have the responsibility to feel the pain of others. This is what compels us to empathize, to sympathize, and to be compassionate.

First Corinthians 12:26 reads: "If one part suffers, every part suffers with it; if one part is honored, every part rejoices with it." The ability to feel the pain of others is a gift given to us and a responsibility we share in following His Word. Steve Camp's song about people suffering from AIDS and HIV infection, "Do You Feel Their Pain?" says it so well:

Do you feel their pain, has it touched your life?
Can you taste the salt in the tears they cry?
Will you love them more than the hate that's been?
Will you love them back to life again?

Are we capable of feeling the pain of people suffering from AIDS? We need to be, if we are to be true to God's calling.

This is not easy, since we must overcome many prejudices and biases in order to suffer with PWAs. We'll discuss prejudices in the next chapter. But the responsibility for us to feel their pain does in fact exist in Scripture. Paul doesn't let us off the hook very easily either. He wrote, "It has been granted to you on behalf of Christ not only to believe on Him, but also to suffer for Him" (Phil. 1:29). The sacrifices we make because we are Christians become real when they cause us to suffer. Paul goes on to say that it is because he follows Christ that he must suffer as he does (2 Tim. 1:11-12).

For those seeking a relationship with God, another value of suffering is given in 1 Peter 4:1: "Therefore, since Christ suffered in His body, arm yourselves also with the same attitude, because he who has suffered in his body is done with sin." What a powerful promise Peter gives us. He goes on to say, "However, if you suffer as a Christian, do not be ashamed, but praise God that you bear that name" (4:16). And he also shares, "If you suffer for doing good and you endure it, this is commendable before God" (2:20).

Certainly Christ's example of suffering for our sake is one which we must weigh carefully as we evaluate how we should respond to the AIDS crisis. Suffering does not entail taking foolhardy risks, nor does it mean that everyone has to experience high levels of physical pain. It simply means that to sacrifice self is a gift to God. By giving to others, we glorify God. We read in Revelation 2:10: "Do not be afraid of what you are about to suffer." Perfect love, we know, drives out fear (see 1 John 4:18).

So, with an understanding of this virus and how it is transmitted, and with an understanding that Christ stopped and stooped to help those who suffered—the lepers and the outcasts—we too are empowered to respond to those suffering from AIDS. We know that if we suffer in the process, we will gain; and if we can help those suffering appreciate what their trials can mean to them in the context of eternal life, we will have acted in a way that is certainly pleasing to God.

IS MANKIND SUFFERING
GOD'S JUDGMENT THROUGH AIDS?

Probably the most difficult part of dealing with the AIDS crisis is trying to understand God's hand in it. As we have stated earlier, the tendency of many in the Christian community, ourselves included when we first saw this disease strike, was to conclude that it was God's judgment. However, since the epidemic has spread, its judgmental nature has been brought into question. Yet many still raise the question—or make the claim—that AIDS is, in fact, God's judgment.

As we have tried to understand God's role in the epidemic, we find ourselves thinking that we need to be very careful in trying to define what God is or is not doing. We believe that the epidemic can pose a trap for some who will get caught up in the business of judging God. Certainly God works in mysterious ways and we all have to endeavor to follow what He would have us do. But that does not necessarily mean that it is for us to know everything He is about.

What becomes important to God, and how we will all be ultimately judged, is the way we respond to others in need. More people in the church are now trying to evaluate what the church's role should be in this epidemic, and fewer are telling us what God has in mind in allowing it to happen. I believe we can all say that the epidemic exists as a result of man not following God's Word and that AIDS is certainly a consequence of man's sinful nature. We need to spend time, therefore, defining how we respond and also what limits us in responding appropriately. This requires dealing with our prejudices and our viewing others as individuals and creations of God—and their sin as a separate issue by itself.

We also need to understand that the suffering we will all endure can be an opportunity for guiding many to eternal life with God. The fire that is necessary to heat steel to the point where it can be shaped into useful objects is like the crucible necessary to shape us into beings which please God. This suffering can create endurance, build character, and generate hope.

To share God's love and eternal promises with those suffering requires the help of many hands. AIDS ministry is not for everyone, but for those who feel called to it, there are great rewards. Many who participate in visiting prisoners, for example, often end up saying that they themselves have been more greatly enriched because of that experience than the individuals to whom they ministered. Now if the church can reach out to people in prison with unconditional love, it can reach out to anyone trapped by AIDS. In so doing, we can each grow in the Lord. Let us no longer judge or question; let us trust and boldly act.

As Helmut Thielicke writes:

> Of course, we, as believing Christians, know just as little as others do why this or that has to come upon us and hurt us. But we know the One who does understand. And we trust in His love. This is our support. If we believe there is loving intent, we can endure. . . . Being loved is more necessary for living than being without pain.[2]

CHAPTER TWELVE

Dealing with Prejudices Regarding AIDS

Prior to our joining the fight against AIDS, I (Shepherd) readily confessed before God that I had a bias against homosexuals and that I thought homosexuality to be a sin above all other sins. What I did not know then but know now is that God works until He gets through to us, particularly when He's not happy with our attitudes. (In other words, never tell God, "I'm with you all the way, but I'm drawing the line on this one exception." That doesn't work.)

The AIDS epidemic and our involvement in it have taught me a great lesson which I freely admit: that is, we must be able to differentiate between individuals and what they do that is displeasing to God. As many church leaders say, we must separate the sin from the sinner. To separate the sin from the sinner, I had to overcome my prejudices, especially toward people who are promiscuous, homosexual, or unfaithful to their spouses.

Anita and I have had the opportunity to meet many individuals involved in the AIDS epidemic. The homosexual community responded first to the crisis because so many of its members were being stricken. Consequently, we, as an AIDS organization, have had to interact with many gay leaders in this issue. God has taken my own pride and prejudices as a result and, as He does so well, put them in perspective.

When we read the passages in Scripture where homosexuality is mentioned, we learn it is not the only sin that displeases God; with it often appear any number of sins to which Christians succumb. Homosexuality, though, is so readily identified with those individuals who participate in it that we often fail to delineate between the act and the individual. Amazingly, homosexuals have every opportunity and right to establish a relationship with God through Christ that heterosexuals have; and those who do are as much children of God as all believers are. In God's eyes, all are sinners who can be redeemed through Christ.

C.S. Lewis commented on this: "The sins of the flesh are bad. . . . For there are two things inside me, competing with the human self which I must try to become. They are the Animal self, and the Diabolical self. The Diabolical self is the worse of the two. That is why a cold, self-righteous prig who goes regularly to church may be far nearer to hell than a prostitute. But, of course, it is better to be neither."[1]

Repentance is certainly the beginning of the process of a full and fulfilling vertical relationship between man and God; it is the individual's decision to change and to follow God's Word. That is each individual's responsibility, not ours. Ours is to evaluate our own relationship with God and change those things which need correcting through the redemptive power of Christ.

Any number of events contributed to my overcoming this prejudice against homosexuals, but perhaps one of the most significant happened in a family who lost their son to AIDS. This Christian family came from a Chicago suburb — an all-American family whose son experimented with sex at a young age and soon found himself, unbeknownst to his family, in a homosexual lifestyle. They learned about it only when he shared with them that he was HIV positive and suffering some of the effects of AIDS.

The family reacted with love. Deeply disappointed about both their son's homosexuality and his illness, they nevertheless felt it their obligation to help him as best they could in the remaining days of his life. The son responded to this love in a very positive way, confessing his sin and reconciling himself to God through Christ.

When he died, his physician approached the parents and said he would be happy to write on the death certificate that the son died of pneumonia. When their pastor

approached them about the funeral service, he also suggested that the cause of death be listed as pneumonia. This
was a hard decision for the family, but after prayer and
thoughtful consideration they concluded that the true
cause of death should be listed as AIDS. They reasoned
this tragedy could be used to God's glory, and asked themselves the question, "How can God use a lie?"

Since then, this family has spoken at numerous churches
to both encourage those who will face similar circumstances and to discourage young people from sexual experimentation which may eventually put them at risk for
contracting this virus, particularly those considering homosexual relationships. What this brave family taught me
was that their precious son was not only their child but
God's child, regardless of what he had done with his life;
and that through Christ he could gain eternal life. I often
think of others in the homosexual lifestyle in the context of
this young man. Then I realize that I must extend the same
type of love to them as these parents did their son, and as
Christ would and did for the many sinners He embraced.

LET HIM WHO IS WITHOUT SIN . . .

Christian singer Steve Camp was forced to confront his
prejudices one day when Dr. Tony Campolo challenged
him to sing about AIDS. "I told him, 'You've got the wrong
guy,' " Steve said, explaining how he got involved with
AIDS ministry to the Dallas concert audience on World
AIDS Day 1989. "He essentially told me my problem was
that I was so 'stinking self-righteous' that I thought I was
better than them. You know, he was right. He nailed me
right between my evangelical eyes. I thought it was important that I keep a little group of people to point to—to say,
'See, Lord, I'm not as bad as them.'

"I was wrong. My self-righteousness was just as bad, or
worse, than someone else's homosexuality. I had to learn
that there is level ground around the cross—we are all
guilty and except for the grace of God we all deserve hell.
But by grace through faith in our Lord Jesus Christ, He has
given us eternal life."

As a result, Steve founded ACCT and today arranges

concerts with other Christian singers and musicians to raise awareness about AIDS in the church and to help others face their own prejudices or self-righteous attitudes which keep them from proclaiming Christ's love.

The church often does not want to acknowledge that members of its body sin in particular ways, most notably sexual sins. However, this epidemic is no respecter of gender and will ultimately be seen most prevalently among heterosexuals, especially those who have more than one sexual partner. The first step, therefore, in being able to deal with those individuals is to acknowledge that their behavior exists and that no sin is too great in the eyes of God to preclude repentance, redemption, and reconciliation.

Most Christians react unfavorably to individuals who are known to have had affairs or who are promiscuous. This is a proper reaction since Scripture teaches us to find sin abhorent and to rid it from our midst. In most cases, it is the sin, not the sinner, that is the object of the Christian's disdain, especially when the sinner is repentant.

However, with sexual sins (particularly homosexuality) this process of separating sin from sinner is often more difficult for Christians. One reason is the destructiveness of sexual sins to the individual and to his or her family.

Another reason today is the threat of transmitting HIV to another person, like an unsuspecting spouse. Finally, sexual sins carry the stigma of being sins of the worst kind.

Promiscuity today may result in both spiritual and physical death, and so it requires the church to deal with the issue forthrightly.

The definition of promiscuity is twofold. First, in the context of unfaithfulness to a marital partner; and second, in the context of single adults or teens who experiment sexually or become addicted where multiple-partner relations occur. In the face of AIDS, either situation carries with it dire consequences.

Scriptures are clear on sexual conduct regarding married and single individuals. Sex is a gift from God to be used only in marriage and which allows for the procreation of mankind. Without sex, none of us would exist; it is, therefore, of inestimable value. But it is also something that can be corrupted. We need to be careful in our messages to young people to never imply that sex is bad. It is more accurate to say that it is unhealthy or inappropriate under the wrong circumstances but joyful within the confines of marriage.

Like it or not, we live in an era when sex sells. It sells clothing. It sells makeup. It sells soft drinks. And it sells young people on the idea that without it life has less meaning. We also live in an age where immediate satisfaction is a primary goal of so many Americans. When a drive for gratification is combined with an erosion of the traditional family unit, we have the makings of an environment where a sexually transmitted disease, if introduced, can run rampant.

That is precisely what is beginning to happen today with HIV infection among our nation's youth and single adults, though it is mostly unseen. From what we know about HIV infection, however, within ten years it will become very apparent that historic proportions of infection began occurring within the heterosexual community in the mid to late 1980s.

Three difficulties exist in giving messages about sex and the dangers of AIDS/HIV. First, there is the inherent response of denial, which causes individuals to discount that infection will happen, or that it will happen to anyone they know, or that it would ever happen to them. Second, the environment in which young people grow up today focuses on the value of sexual activity before and outside of marriage. Third, because HIV infection has not yet resulted in symptomatic AIDS in large numbers of heterosexuals, it is not totally accepted that this will become or is already a heterosexual epidemic.

In addressing denial, we must first realize that it exists, especially among people who wish to pursue their own objectives rather than the Lord's. We once learned of an evangelical minister who was participating in an adulterous relationship. Because of the way he perceived the relationship, he had rationalized that he was not really committing adultery. If a well-schooled minister can rationalize intimate physical contact with someone outside of his marriage, then it is not hard to believe that young people can even more readily justify the expression of nearly any fleshly urge or physical pleasure.

What's more, to overcome the temptations of this world, we must clearly establish for young people options that will allow them to have satisfying enjoyment in the context of the Judeo-Christian belief system. We must also help them develop refusal skills which will allow them to say no and not succumb to peer pressure. Adult believers must serve as examples for our youth in our own behavioral habits so they seek to emulate us, not unhealthy role models. The challenge Paul gives us is to try to imitate him even as he imitates Christ. That is a mandate for all adults in the context of sexual morality in the age of AIDS.

Finally, we must be able to show instances where young people have become infected by HIV through heterosexual activity. As we learn of infections, we must use these as examples (without breaching confidentiality) to reach our youth about the dangers and consequences of HIV infection. Beyond that, we need to encourage young people who feel they may have been exposed to the virus to be tested.

JUDGE NOT, LEST YOU BE JUDGED

The idea of working with people addicted to drugs is repulsive to many people. The stereotype of the drug addict is the individual hiding in an alley with a rubber band around his arm, injecting a needle into a raised vein. However, that's a stereotype and not reflective of reality. Even among IV-drug users, a very significant percentage of drug abuse is recreational (defined as primarily weekend or occasional use).

The list of actual drug abusers would include the working man or woman, the student, or the government employee of any race who, mostly off the job (but sometimes on the job), routinely use some form of narcotic. By definition, most narcotics are addictive and abusive. If drug abuse parallels sexual activity in the church, then we also have a significant problem to deal with in our own house. The church can no longer sit back and say that drug abuse is "their problem." Like HIV infection, drug abuse is our society's problem, our community's problem, and very much the church's problem. We need not point fingers at the inner-city or the minority member or the high-school dropout. We need only point back at our own communities.

The relationship of drug abuse to HIV infection is as simple as it is significant. Individuals who inject drugs often acquire the HIV virus through sharing drugs, needles, or associated paraphernalia (syringes, bowls, and so on). In addition, people who deal drugs may exchange them for sex, and those who take drugs use sex to raise funds for more drugs.

Because of HIV infection, this cycle of abuse will result in the deaths of countless individuals. When this happens, some say, "Good riddance." Such thinking removes the concept of God's holiness from humanity. It also ignores the fact that allowing the virus to become so well established would ultimately prove harmful to each and every community nationwide.

So, as we educate our young people we must make clear the connection between drug abuse and HIV infection. As we list their dangers, we must be alert to see if any youth are already involved in drug abuse. As we mentioned in regard to sexual education, care needs to be taken not to create in our youth curiosity about drugs so they are tempted to try them.

We take our hats off to organizations and parties that have been active in educating the public on the dangers of drug abuse, such as Teen Challenge, Covenant House, Youth for Christ's Youth Guidance Program, the "Just Say No" program, Congressman Charles Rangel, former drug director William Bennett, HHS Secretary Louis Sullivan, plus all those working in the private sector and in government to end the consumption of illegal drugs in America.

The same societal pressures that cause young people to pursue promiscuous sexual activity also push young people to become involved in substance abuse. When one considers that drug stores are found in every shopping mall and on every major street in every community, and that medicine cabinets in private homes are also full of drugs, it is little wonder that our youth cannot understand why drug use is wrong. We must articulate the differences between legitimate drug taking for medical purposes and the use of drugs for recreational or fleeting physical pleasures.

Young people need to understand that once they start experimenting with drugs, it is incredibly difficult to stop. Again, we must instill positive behavioral patterns early on so that young people will not have to wrestle with behavioral changes as they grow into their teen and adult years.

Scripture contains the answers to a healthy life without drug dependencies. We are admonished to not overindulge in anything, to keep ourselves healthy, and to not seek pleasures induced by drugs or alcohol (drunken pleasures). Most important, we must share with young people that drug abuse today carries with it yet another killer and another reason to avoid such behavior—AIDS. Responding to this critical need will remove some unfounded prejudices while reinforcing some justifiable fears.

FOR ALL HAVE SINNED

The Greek word for sin means to "miss the mark." What is the mark? And how do we know when we've missed it?

When we think of sin within the church, it is often in the context of the other person's sin rather than our own. We each tend to be great "speck removers." We also want to believe, largely as a result of denial, that God is going to judge the other individual for his or her sinfulness, not us.

Since involving ourselves in the AIDS issue, we have dealt with many Christians who have been devastated not just by the virus but by the judgment of their fellow believers.

One young Christian woman died alone from AIDS in a nursing home without the benefit of her pastor's comfort and spiritual counsel. He was not there because he refused to be in the same room with her.

Another extended family—all Christians—is being torn apart because one member is infected. Some members have rallied to support the infected relative while others have totally rejected that relative; those attempting to reconcile both sides are being ripped to emotional shreds, not fully accepted by those on either side of the battle line.

Equally tragic is the plight of a West Coast family we have been helping. Because the mother was transfused over 70 units of blood in the early '80s, she was later tested for HIV. Though she initially tested negative, the family was not allowed to become members of the church they were attending after sharing their concerns with the pastor and elders. Heartbroken, the family moved to another area where the Metropolitan Community Church (a largely gay church) welcomed them. The family was afraid to go to their denominational church for help.

The HIV virus cannot tell the difference between sinners and saints. It only knows people by their white blood cells and will infect anyone who comes into intimate contact with an infected individual. So the lesson in regard to HIV infection is that if we don't each abide by the will of God, then we may each end up on the list of those who have become HIV positive.

In order to positively impact the AIDS crisis, we must be exceedingly careful to overcome our own prejudices. Rather than judging others, we must take care to see PWAs as God's creation; then their sins will not be roadblocks to our reaching out in compassion and care. Christ reached out to the adulterous woman and, only after helping and winning her confidence, advised her to go and sin no more. Those who have a free hand will be able to reach out. But those whose hands are filled with stones will have a difficult time in responding as Christ would have them respond.

Christ nurtured no prejudices that hindered His speaking to the Samaritan woman at the well (see John 4), though His disciples would have had nothing to do with her. And because of that love-motivated contact, she was later able to share with others, so that "many of the Samaritans from that town believed in Him because of the woman's testimony."

Unless we Christians overcome our prejudices about AIDS and PWAs, we will never be able to have conversations which may lead them to eternal life.

The first wave of AIDS has washed over many needy communities of people: the homeless, the destitute, the homosexuals, the drug abusers, the sexually promiscuous. The second wave will hit communities closer to home: our churches, our young, our friends and neighbors. If we are to help, we are to help all. The first step in doing that is to follow Christ's example and overcome our prejudices and our fears.

As an AIDS organization, we have interacted with many other groups involved in this issue, many of which are predominantly gay in focus and membership. Toward the end of the '80s, this type of contact began to change significantly as cases involving minorities, women, and children brought more and more heterosexual individuals to the issue. The establishment of ACCT and other local ministries throughout the country also brought in more of mainstream America and the church. It was lonely for a while; but now we have lots of friends.

Some of those friends have worked with this issue longer than we. Some of those people are gay. I (Shepherd) had lunch one day with the executive director of a major national AIDS organization. I was able to express mutual concerns with this individual, who is unfortunately in later-stage disease. While I had no fear of sharing a meal and even sharing some food from a common plate, I had a great sense of sadness and loss, since this person—created in the image of God—would soon no longer be with us.

Another friend is uninfected and I want desperately to see him insulate himself from the possibility of infection—ideally to see him involved in a marriage in which he could raise children. I would be grief-stricken if I were to learn he had become infected, for he has admirable qualities, a keen mind, and unlimited potential.

Our relationship has allowed me to share with him my understanding of what God expects of us and what He finds pleasing and not pleasing. Yet, had I not been able to overcome my own biases and prejudices, I would have never had this wonderful opportunity to get to know these people and to share with them. Regardless of how they ultimately decide to live, I will continually extend God's love and mine to them.

This does not mean that I, Anita, or ASAP in any way support the homosexual political agenda or lifestyle. To the contrary, we have argued effectively that AIDS should be handled from a medical/public health perspective, and that anyone using the issue to advance other agendas is wrong to do so—including those wanting to advance gay rights or wanting to quarantine homosexuals.

Because we have, with God's help, overcome our prejudices, we have been able to act in the AIDS issue calmly, rationally, eyeball to eyeball in ways which show respect for each individual as God's creation and fellow human being.

On a personal note, I would say that if I was able to overcome such strong prejudices, virtually anyone in Christendom can. But I also believe that evil forces can blind us from doing what God would have us do. And I believe prejudices are perhaps among the most diabolical weapons used against Christians. Yes, we can imitate Christ and please God. And certainly this epidemic, tragic as it is, can yield good. It is actually an opportunity for each individual Christian to fulfill his or her commitment to God.

CHAPTER THIRTEEN

The Individual Christian's Role in the AIDS Epidemic

By now it must be obvious to you that we are extremely committed to fighting AIDS/HIV while caring for those affected by it. As we have explained previously, this commitment is fueled by many factors: our concern for our own children's well-being; our feeling of responsibility to future generations on this planet; the mandate to follow the Lord's leading in our lives; our love and concern for our friends who are infected; and our desire to be like Christ.

ARE YOU CALLED?

But we don't believe we can or should tell you what God wants you to do with your life. Yes, we can point you to scriptural commands to do good works and show your faith through action, but we cannot presume to tell you that you are being led to involvement in AIDS-related ministry. So many needs are crying for Christian commitment and action: homelessness, illiteracy, substance abuse, child abuse, the hungry, the elderly. We could name a host of other needs and so could you. But we are not here to tell you that AIDS is more important than any of those problems the church must face—only that it is equally important to any of them. Probably AIDS will impact all of those things directly or indirectly.

Scripture teaches that we are all parts of one body. We

hear many sermons about that concept, particularly as it
relates to our gifts. Possibly we hear the "one body—many
functions" theme preached frequently because it is so true.
We do not believe that all Christians will be called to take
PWAs into their homes. Not every Christian will be led to
visit them in the hospital. Not all will commit to long-term
work with substance abusers who are HIV positive.

But we do believe that some will be called to fill each of
these roles and even more. The reality of any ministry in
the church is that committed people are needed at all levels to make the ministry work effectively. If all of us are
visiting in the hospitals and no one is working to support
families dealing with infection, effective ministry will not
take place. If all of us are giving money to AIDS ministry
and none of us are praying for those touched by the epidemic, effective ministry will not take place. All points in
the ministry chain are vital.

One need not be in actual AIDS ministry to lend a helping hand. An alert Christian in Nebraska called one day to
say he was a member of the local school board, and that a
young man attending the school named Matt was HIV positive from his Factor VIII medication. The board member
asked for guidance in doing the right thing: namely, helping Matt and his family, protecting faculty and fellow students, and being a proper witness for Christ.

What occurred was remarkable. The school board members did not panic; instead, they brought in experts who
explained what the actual risks were and that people did
not have to fear HIV. Transcripts of the town meeting show
people asking how they could help; headlines proclaimed
"AIDS Can Bring Out the Best in People"; and best of all,
Matt now enjoys the total support of all his classmates and
friends.

We hope this book will help many more persons like
Matt find acceptance and, in particular, support from their
churches.

Throughout the preceding chapters we have enumerated
a number of opportunities for direct AIDS-related ministry—situations involving those directly infected and affected by HIV. Other ministry possibilities exist within the
community that are crucial to changing the face of the
issue. We'd like to list some of them here.

MINISTER IN YOUR COMMUNITY

☐ One of the primary tasks we have is to change the way AIDS/HIV is viewed by the public. Our goal is to "normalize" and "destigmatize" the disease in order to make it more a concern of middle America. As you have seen from this text, the reality is that AIDS will, in fact, affect middle America in enormous ways. As a society and a church, we need to accept the need to prepare for the day when we begin seeing infection in our own congregations. You can help change public attitude by discussing the issue. When others are prejudiced and make erroneous statements related to the epidemic, be sure you give the accurate information or counteract their bias in an appropriate way.

Another way to help destigmatize the disease is to treat it like any other when talking to friends about societal or medical issues. Be matter-of-fact about AIDS/HIV, the medical facts, and statistics. As you accept the reality of AIDS and are unafraid to face it, you will lead others to do the same.

☐ Your local school, in all likelihood, has some form of health education or family life curriculum. Find out what is being taught, without being confrontive. In case your school is looking for curricula to institute, become familiar with the many courses focusing on chastity that are available for public schools and gather recommendations. Then, in a positive, constructive way, work toward the day when your school will be ready to incorporate a curricula that will reflect the optimal medical and prevention messages we've discussed.

☐ Civic organizations, professional clubs, and other community groups may have avoided discussing AIDS/HIV in their meetings, or they may simply not have thought of it. Bring the issue up, when appropriate, in circles where you are involved. Offer to set up a meeting, panel, or discussion group on the topic in a way that would fit into the group's goals and format.

☐ One key area that relates to AIDS/HIV today and in the future is legislation. Every state will pass AIDS-related bills. Contact your state legislators to learn what your state is doing. Learn which legislators are working on the issue and what their views are. Find a legislator that shares your concerns and perspective and support his or her efforts. ASAP has worked with legislators in more than half of the states. If you write to ASAP at the address listed in the beginning of the Leader's Guide, we will be happy to give you names of persons to contact.

☐ Learn what the federal government is doing about AIDS. The National AIDS Commission (NAC) was appointed by Congress to follow up on the findings of the Presidential Commission on the Human Immunodeficiency Virus Epidemic. Find out what the NAC is doing. Contact your congressman and senators and let them know about your concern for this issue. Many in Washington have not involved themselves in the AIDS issue because their constituents have not shown any interest. Let your voice be heard. Let your representatives know that you are watching their activities and votes related to AIDS/HIV.

☐ When you learn of someone active in AIDS/HIV ministry locally, statewide, or nationally, write him or her a note of support and encouragement. Often the work is lonely and the tasks seem insurmountable. Your kind word would go far to minister to those who are overburdened.

☐ Donate to existing AIDS ministries and organizations. Some groups have nearly had to stop their ministry due to lack of financial support. Other evangelicals involved in the issue find great cooperation and acceptance from local government and institutions but little from the church. You will want to research groups carefully to ensure they conform to your objectives in this issue before donating.

☐ Take or make opportunities to tell young people about the risks of behaviors that provide opportunity for HIV transmission to occur. Spend time talking with neighborhood kids, the baby-sitter, your children's friends, or teens at your church in a friendly, informal way about AIDS. Let them know you're open to talking to them about the issues.

☐ Pray regularly for those infected, affected, and ministering in this arena.

☐ Pray regularly that God will continually guide you in the direction He has for your personal ministry.

☐ Pray regularly that medical scientists will find effective treatments, vaccines, or a cure; and that all those in-fected will have access to health care.

We pray that God will lead some reading this book to become actively involved in this issue. AIDS-related ministry is not easy work, but then, very few worthwhile ministries are. Some of our friends thought us foolish to get involved; others wondered what we had been doing or dealing with that we hadn't told them about; still others criticized us for focusing on AIDS rather than evangelizing the homosexual community. But once we understood God's path for us, it was impossible to turn aside or away from it — regardless of the apathy or comments of others.

One frequent criticism has come from those who do not want to believe that the epidemic is spreading. Some, in the face of what we believe is irrefutable evidence, still maintain that the epidemic is contained. This attitude does, though, make rationalizing noninvolvement easier. These people say we're overreacting, scaring people needlessly, and wasting our time and lives.

Our response is that, first, even if this virus were only to affect the populations already infected today, it would still be our issue. We as Christians would still be commanded to respond. And second, no one would be happier than we to be wrong about the disease's severity. However, we believe the spread of AIDS has reached epidemic proportions, based on the data we have researched and gathered.

In addition, we learn daily of other statistics and studies that confirm what our information has shown us. If we were wrong in our basic facts about AIDS/HIV, then our focus on responsible behavior for the general public — and the practice of holiness for Christians — would have simply inconvenienced some people, possibly denying them some physical satisfaction. If we're right, though, and the epidemic is all we believe it to be, then we will have saved actual lives. We're willing to take that risk.

One of the misconceptions we fear exists is that people involved in AIDS work have to be either conservative or liberal firebrands. Now we are not alarmists by nature. We are educated, reserved, somewhat intelligent people who try to act and react responsibly and in keeping with God's Word. And the truth is that the AIDS crisis needs to draw in greater numbers of thinking, considerate, and caring individuals who will go about the work of service rather than grandstanding on the issues involved.

As the epidemic continues to spread, the politics of AIDS will be moot, from what we can see, and the rhetoric just so much hot air. In the end, the compassion, the caring, the involvement, and the changing of lives are what will make the difference to the Lord and to the people so tragically affected by this disease.

More and more Christians are touched by this need. For instance, one young woman on the brink of a critical career decision has chosen to pursue an AIDS-related profession. Her brother is HIV positive.

A pastor in New York City adopted a son who was HIV positive. "It made a big difference in people," he says. "It helped them learn to deal with the disease when they had personal contact with someone infected. Many come up to me now and tell me they can care about their infected neighbor or friend because they knew my son." When that precious boy died, cards from more than 2,000 people were on the walls of his room, all from people whose lives he had touched.

The people of God are responding, as they have historically, to the call to serve in His name. Once we taste the fruits of service, nothing could persuade us to do anything but serve. Our lives are enriched beyond description. We are among those who can say without reservation that, because of AIDS, our lives will never again be the same.

One young Christian woman became infected and sent a written testimony to a friend:

> How can I be anything else but glad? He saved my soul, He saved my marriage. He saved my husband, He saved my life. He allowed me to see the joy set before me so that I have gladly been able to endure my cross. I get to have inner happiness in a time when that is humanly impossible. . . . This thing will break us financially. To my shame we will have to depend on others for food, shelter, bills, medicine, doctors' visits, and on and on and on. The human sacrifice on our behalf is amazing. We are indebted to so many — for so much — we can never repay it. Never! It is humiliating. It's humbling. . . . I can't repay my debts, but the Lord can. Every believer that gives me time, love, attention, financial support, strokes, hugs, pray-

ers, patience, and so much more, gets credit as though he has given those things to Jesus Christ Himself. If they do it to "the least of these"—they do it also for Him. I love to think of the rewards in eternity waiting for those who have given so much of themselves on account of me.

Reflecting on the epidemic, his faith, and the impact AIDS will have on all of us, Dr. Robert Redfield commented:

> I try to teach my daughter to be a Christian, but she doesn't understand why we hurry by the homeless man on the grate as we go down the street. The next century is the ultimate opportunity for the Christian community in this world. We have tried for 2,000 years to actually live our value system. But today as a nation our priorities are totally valueless.
>
> I view our nation as a family in crisis. Where do people go when they're in crisis? They go back to the core values to survive. We now have the opportunity to make our core values the way the world lives. So when I walk down the street with my daughter and see five men huddled to get warm on the grate, we don't just hurry by.

Won't you consider becoming a Samaritan alongside the many others already working to bind up the wounds of our nation caused by this epidemic—to offer compassion, healing, and ultimately eternal life through Christ?

LEADER'S GUIDE

Introduction

The Leader's Guide is designed to offer ideas and resources for anyone using this book as the basis of a study of AIDS, the church, and the individual Christian. The text itself is divided into four 3-chapter sections, with an introductory chapter which offers an overview of the content to come. This 13-chapter format is designed to fit easily into a Sunday School curriculum for adults or teens, or any other church program. Some chapters could easily be combined to accommodate a shorter curriculum time frame.

This guide will contain ideas for studying each chapter, including: the stated goal for the chapter, various approaches that can be taken to the material, appropriate Scripture, discussion starters, outside activities, application activities, and additional resources. At some point before the session ends, take time to pray through the points in the "Prayer Focus" as a group. This section is for use in or out of sessions to target AIDS-related concerns. All study elements are designed to promote a balanced spiritual, practical, and personal approach to AIDS/HIV.

To make the study as worthwhile as possible, contact sources for free AIDS/HIV information, brochures, and other materials early so they will be available to group members throughout the study. Books, larger pamphlets, and video and audio cassettes can be gathered for a "lending library" for group members during the course.

Some sources of free materials and/or information are:

National AIDS Information Clearinghouse
P.O. Box 6003
Rockville, MD 20850
800/458-5231

American Red Cross National AIDS Education Program
1730 D. St., NW
Washington, D.C. 20006
202/639-3223
(Your local American Red Cross chapter may also have materials.)

Your county Public Health director.

Your state AIDS coordinator.

AIDS Crisis and Christians Today (ACCT)
P.O. Box 24647
Nashville, TN 37202-4647
615/371-1616

Americans for a Sound AIDS/HIV Policy (ASAP)
P.O. Box 17433
Washington, D.C. 20041
703/471-7350

LEADER'S GUIDE/CHAPTER 1

This chapter contains an overview of material, touching briefly on topics to be discussed in greater detail in later chapters. Ideas outlined here are meant to lay the groundwork for future discussion and study.

GOAL
To recognize AIDS/HIV as a wide-ranging issue which will demand response on many fronts from the institutional church as well as the individual Christian.

APPROACH
1. Divide the group into several subgroups which will concentrate on collecting information on specific AIDS-related subjects

for use in future study. Participants may choose their subgroups based on interest or expertise. Cover topics such as:

medical facts	ministry opportunities
human behaviors	prevention
the family	the church's role in society
education issues	church policy
legislation: federal,	legal issues: discrimination,
state, local	confidentiality, and so on

Give each subgroup a specific assignment to prepare for future meetings, for example: clipping articles on AIDS/HIV; exploring ministry opportunities in your community and state; collecting examples of AIDS education curriculum, media messages, and local school policy; obtaining copies of local ordinances and state and federal laws related to AIDS; investigating AIDS-related activity sponsored by your denomination or local church groups.

2. As a group, decide on several scriptural concepts to be studied for their bearing on AIDS, the church, and the individual Christian. Refer to a source such as *Unger's Bible Dictionary*. These subjects could include (but are not limited to):

affliction	plague
mercy	leper
disease (treatment)	judgment

These studies can be done by subgroups within the meeting or individually as an outside assignment.

Choose either of the following to do for the meeting.

3. Invite a speaker to address your group who has personal experience with AIDS. This will make the disease real to those who have not met anyone infected or affected by HIV. Your guest could be a person with AIDS, a friend or family member of someone infected, or a health-care professional working with AIDS patients.

4. Play a video or audiotape about AIDS to introduce the general topic to the group and foster discussion.

SCRIPTURE

Luke 10:25-37	Romans 5:1-5
James 1:2	Matthew 5:1-16
Luke 5:29-32	Psalm 130
Matthew 8:3-4; Luke 5:12-14	Matthew 25:31-46

PRAYER FOCUS

Families who have suffered because of infection; infected family members; churches where families are touched by infection (which may or may not know about the illness in their midst); members of the study groups who are seeking knowledge and direction in this issue.

DISCUSSION QUESTIONS
1. What is HIV?
2. What is AIDS?
3. How has your family reacted to news stories about AIDS?
4. What concerns you most about the epidemic?
5. Describe your emotions as you think and talk about AIDS.
6. Examine the Parable of the Good Samaritan. What principles does it offer related to the AIDS epidemic?
7. Often those infected with HIV are called modern-day lepers. Study the discussion and treatment of lepers in Scriptures such as Leviticus 13:1-46; 14:1-32; Luke 17:12-14. Evaluate similarities and differences between the two diseases. Based on Scripture, what conclusions can be drawn or guidelines devised for dealing with today's AIDS epidemic in the church?

You may also prepare special discussion questions to follow up any audiovisual presentations you make.

DISCUSSION/APPLICATION
Ask group members to submit written questions they want answered in the course, or to openly raise their questions, concerns, and fears at the outset of the study. (Ask a clerk to record all questions and comments that group members raise at the beginning.) These questions should be reviewed by the leader and could be given to subgroups to focus on in future meetings. These questions can also be used at the end of the course as a recap of information or post-study "test."

OUTSIDE ACTIVITY
1. Have group members clip articles and ads related to AIDS/HIV. These can be filed each week by category and used for future discussion.
2. Ask group members to go to the local library or bookstore to find one book on AIDS to read during the course of the study. These could include suggested titles in the Leader's Guide.
3. Have group members keep journals of their thoughts, feelings, and understanding about AIDS/HIV throughout the study.

RESOURCES
Surgeon General's Report on Acquired Immune Deficiency Syndrome. Available from National AIDS Information Clearinghouse, 800/458-5231. Pamphlet, free.

Responding to the Challenge of AIDS: A Resource Guide for Congregations. Mennonite Mutual AIDS, P.O. Box 483, Goshen, IN 46526; 900/348-7468. Pamphlet, $2.00.

A Realistic Look at AIDS: Interview with Robert R. Redfield, Jr., M.D. by James Dobson (1988), Focus on the Family. Audiotape.

Joining Hands to Fight a Common Enemy by Frank Young, M.D., Ph.D., former Commissioner of the Food and Drug Administration; *The AIDS Epidemic and Your Local Church* by the Reverend Lon Solomon (1989) ASAP. Audiotape, suggested contribution $6.00.

The Church's Response to the AIDS/HIV Epidemic: A Guideline for Education and Policy Development. ASAP. Booklet, suggested contribution, $5.00.

LEADER'S GUIDE/CHAPTER 2

GOAL
To gain an accurate understanding of the HIV virus, the disease it causes, its transmission, and the manifestation of the illness over time.

APPROACH (Choose one.)
1. Ask a physician or nurse in the congregation to attend the meeting and explain the HIV virus and facts about AIDS.
2. Play a video or audiotape which will help explain the medical facts of HIV.
3. Invite your local public health director, an infectious disease specialist in the community, or a medical missionary supported by your church who has dealt with AIDS to address the group and explain the medical aspects of the virus.

SCRIPTURE
Proverbs 8:1-12; 10:13-14; 15:7; 19:2, 25; 20:15
Ecclesiastes 7:12; 9:13-18
James 3:17

PRAYER FOCUS
Scientists, clinicians, and physicians working on developing treatments for people infected with HIV. Health-care workers

who provide daily medical assistance for PWAs.

DISCUSSION QUESTIONS
1. What role does knowledge about HIV play in one's ability to serve God?
2. List the simplified medical facts about HIV—the infection and the disease it causes.
3. List the theories or unclear areas related to medical knowledge of HIV.
4. Discuss what the knowledge of medical facts about HIV means to the church in general and the individual Christian.

DISCUSSION/APPLICATION
Discuss beliefs and ideas that group members had about AIDS/HIV which were changed by the presentation of medical facts. List (and save for later) any questions participants have that are still not answered satisfactorily.

OUTSIDE ACTIVITY
Submit any unanswered questions to a physician or AIDS organization for further clarification.

RESOURCES
Answers about AIDS, American Council on Science and Health, 1995 Broadway, 16th Floor, New York, NY 10023-5860; 212/362-7044. $3.00 plus postage.

Scientific American, October 1988 issue. 415 Madison Ave., New York, NY 10017; 212/754-0550.

Understanding the Immune System by Lydia Woods Schindler, NIH Publication No. 88-529, U.S. Dept. of Health and Human Services, Washington, D.C. 20201.

Update on the Medical Status of the HIV Epidemic and Symptomatic AIDS, Lt. Col. Robert R. Redfield, Jr., M.D., ASAP. Audiotape, suggested contribution $6.00.

LEADER'S GUIDE/CHAPTER 3

GOAL
To gain a clear picture of the epidemic's makeup, of who is infected today, and of the implications for the future.

APPROACH (Choose one.)
1. Identify writings by Christian and secular authors relating to epidemics or plagues. Read excerpts to provide a perspective on dealing with widespread disease, or divide into subgroups to read and discuss selected writings.
2. Invite an older member of the congregation who has witnessed the effects of a past epidemic to explain how it impacted the nation, the community, the church, and the family.
3. Research public response to leprosy over the ages and how cultures have reacted to it.

SCRIPTURE

James 5:13-16   2 Corinthians 12:7-10
Psalm 41:1-3   Galatians 4:12-14
Luke 5:15-20; 13:10-13

PRAYER FOCUS
Nations of the world affected by the epidemic; political and religious leaders of nations devastated by HIV infection, particularly in Central and East Africa; missionaries serving in nations with high infection rates.

DISCUSSION QUESTIONS
1. Examine the role epidemics have played in history.
2. Track how HIV has evolved as a world epidemic.
3. Study the response of the culture of Christ's day to lepers.
4. Note Christ's response and that of His followers to people suffering from serious illness, and compare it with the general response of their culture.

DISCUSSION/APPLICATION
Compare the response to AIDS/HIV among individual Christians and the corporate church with Christ's responses toward lepers and the general attitude of His day.

OUTSIDE ACTIVITY
1. Contact the local public health department or a state legislator to get information on the number of local and state AIDS cases reported.
2. Contact local hospitals, nursing homes, and STD clinics to learn if they have patients with AIDS and to volunteer to do visiting or assisting.

RESOURCES
AIDS: A War We Can Win by David Pence, M.D., The Committee to Stop AIDS, P.O. Box 10517, Minneapolis, MN 55458, $2.00.

Crisis: Heterosexual Behavior in the Age of AIDS by William
H. Masters, M.D., Virginia E. Johnson, and Robert C. Kolodny,
M.D. (1988) Grove Press, New York.

AIDS and The Positive Alternatives by Margaret White, M.D.
(1988) Zondervan Publishing House, Grand Rapids.

*Critical Issues: AIDS/Acquired Immune Deficiency Syn-
drome*, The Christian Life Commission of the Southern Baptist
Church, P.O. Box 25266, Nashville, TN 37202-5266. Pamphlet,
single copy free.

AIDS: Anatomy of a Crisis by Dr. D. James Kennedy, Coral
Ridge Ministries, P.O. Box 40, Ft. Lauderdale, FL 33308;
305/772-0404. Videotape, 58 minutes.

LEADER'S GUIDE/CHAPTER 4

GOAL
To identify the specific impact the AIDS/HIV epidemic will have
on all facets of society.

APPROACH
1. Produce graphs or charts of epidemic statistics that will help
participants picture the size of the epidemic today and how it is
projected to grow.
Choose either of the following for the meeting.
2. Invite a hospital administrator, nursing home administrator,
or other health-care professional in a management role to speak
about the future of the epidemic and its impact on health
care.
3. Set up a panel consisting of representatives of various segments of society involved in and impacted by the AIDS crisis:
health-care administrator, ministry representative, stock analyst,
educator, insurance executive, and so on. Each should discuss
how the epidemic will impact his or her specific profession and
then explain the reactions to the epidemic in his or her
profession.

SCRIPTURE
  Isaiah 58:9-11   Luke 4:36
  Romans 8:18-25   Philippians 1:19-20
  2 Corinthians 4:16–5:8   Romans 15:1-6

PRAYER FOCUS
A personal understanding of the epidemic and what it means to the church, the community, the state, the nation, and the individual.

DISCUSSION QUESTIONS
1. Name professions and industries in the U.S. that the AIDS epidemic will impact. Weigh the degree of impact on each.
2. Find examples in Scripture of those who lived through tragedy or suffering with another. Describe events and interactions. How do these individuals provide models for us as we face the present and future AIDS crises?
3. List different segments of the American population affected by the epidemic; give the extent of present and projected impact.
4. Discuss events which have occurred in this generation which might give us an idea of the impact the epidemic will have. Evaluate their effect on individuals and the nation.
5. Discuss what sacrifices we should be willing to make or what programs should be implemented in the face of the future epidemic.

DISCUSSION/APPLICATION
Ask individuals to project for themselves, based on their professions and extended families, how the future epidemic will impact them.

RESOURCES
AIDS and the Church by Earl E. Shelp and Ronald H. Sunderland (1987) Westminster Press, 925 Chestnut St., Philadelphia, PA 19107; 215/928-2733.

When AIDS Comes to Church by William E. Amos, Jr. (1988) Westminster Press, 925 Chestnut St., Philadelphia, PA 19107; 215/928-2733.

AIDS: A Christian Perspective by Dick Day and C. Everett Koop, M.D. (1989) Word Publishing Co., P.O. Box 1790, Waco, TX 76703; 817/772-7650. Videotape, 40 minutes.

LEADER'S GUIDE/CHAPTER 5

GOAL
To come to individual and group conclusions on the appropriate response to the epidemic on the part of the Christian church.

APPROACH
1. Ask members to share any opportunities for ministry they have passed up in their lifetimes and what effects that had on them, both immediate and long-term.
2. Ask members to discuss opportunities for ministry that they took and what effects that had on them, both immediate and long-term.

SCRIPTURE

1 John 2:4-6; 3:16-20	Matthew 21:18-19
1 Corinthians 2:16; 10:24	Luke 9:23-24; 13:18-20
Matthew 5:1-16	Hebrews 10:24
Colossians 1:10	James 2:22, 24

PRAYER FOCUS
Your local church, your denomination, your friends, your family, yourself as you all learn your respective roles to play in this epidemic.

DISCUSSION QUESTIONS
1. Explain the Bible's perspective on service or ministry.
2. List characteristics of those who perform service or ministry.
3. Evaluate your church's existing programs to discern its priorities (how money is spent, how staff time is allocated, which programs are highly visible, and so on).
4. Discuss changes or additions that could be made to programs evaluated in #3 in light of AIDS and the needs of the '90s.
5. Discuss how scriptural examples portray the process of listening to God before taking action. Relate the process to becoming involved in AIDS-related ministry.

DISCUSSION/APPLICATION
Discuss the balance between ministry within the church and to society at large. What is appropriate and how do the church and individual Christians maintain that balance?

OUTSIDE ACTIVITIES
1. Evaluate your personal daily activities — how much time spent in prayer for ministry, planning for ministry, or doing some form of ministry.
2. Survey the community to learn about AIDS related ministries that may already exist.

RESOURCES
Go Toward the Light by Chris Oyler (1988), Harper & Row Publishers, New York.

In Sickness and in Health: A Story of Love in the Shadow of AIDS by Shirleen Perry with Gregg Lewis (1989), InterVarsity Press, Downers Grove, Illinois.

The AIDS Epidemic: A Challenge to the Church by Penny Pullen, National Association of Evangelicals, P.O. Box 28, Wheaton, IL 60189; 708/665-0500. Audiotape, $5.00.

The Challenges the Epidemic Poses to the Church by Eunice Diaz, ASAP. Audiotape, suggested contribution $6.00.

In Sickness and in Health (1989), InterVarsity Press, Downers Grove, Illinois. Videotape, 35 minutes.

LEADER'S GUIDE/CHAPTER 6

GOAL
To review information discussed to date, to reinforce knowledge, discover areas in question, and prepare to change focus to specific ministry.

APPROACH (Choose one.)
1. Invite the pastor or a lay leader to share obstacles and challenges to AIDS ministry within your community.
2. Invite a representative of an AIDS ministry or other organization working with PWAs to address the challenges of ministry.

SCRIPTURE
James 3:17-18; 4:17   Matthew 22:34-40
Luke 15   1 John 3:18

PRAYER FOCUS
The church in the United States and throughout the world addressing the issue; for guidance that it will understand where to begin and how to proceed. Pray that your congregation will be open to ministry to the hurting, especially those with AIDS.

DISCUSSION QUESTIONS
1. Use questions in the text as a springboard. Are there any other questions related to materials covered that have not been answered?
2. How do the parables in Luke 15 give direction for an approach to the AIDS/HIV issue?

DISCUSSION/APPLICATION
Ask the group members to voice questions they want answered in the balance of the sessions. Ask them to privately list one or two personal goals related to this study that they would like to accomplish by the end of the study.

LEADER'S GUIDE/CHAPTER 7

GOAL
To examine the ministry opportunities related to AIDS to enable group members to begin to see where they might want to be involved in ministry.

APPROACH
1. Make up a panel of persons involved in a variety of ministries of the church to discuss how AIDS/HIV ministry could fit into their existing programs.
2. As a group, decide on a ministry-related project for the group to accomplish by the end of the study.

SCRIPTURE
Hebrews 3:1-3	James 2:8
Galatians 5:14	Romans 13:10
Matthew 5:43-48; 18:21-35;	Ephesians 2:10
21:28-32; 22:39	John 13:34

PRAYER FOCUS
People with AIDS who need ministry. Pray that AIDS ministries and ASAP will have guidance, support, and wisdom in meeting the challenges of the issue.

DISCUSSION QUESTIONS
1. What are your church's AIDS ministry opportunities?
2. Evaluate this list for areas most needed in your community.
3. What are the obstacles in (a) you, (b) your church, and (c) your community to performing AIDS ministry? By following Scripture, how can you overcome those obstacles?
4. Discuss which areas of need would fit into existing church programs.

DISCUSSION/APPLICATION
Ask group members to share two or three Scriptures which speak to them most pointedly about AIDS-related ministry.

OUTSIDE ACTIVITY
Challenge group members to work individually or together on a liturgy or special features that could be used in other church programs to begin instructing your church about AIDS/HIV.

RESOURCES
Care Models and Ministering to Those in Need, panel on AIDS ministry, ASAP. Audiotape, suggested contribution $6.00.

How Will I Tell My Mother? by Jerry Arterburn (1988) Thomas Nelson Publishers, Nashville.

A Christian Response to the AIDS Crisis (1989), The Church of the Nazarene, 6401 The Paseo, Kansas City, MO 64131. Videotape.

AIDS Ministry and Community-Based Organization Models by Jeffrey Collins, Jonathan Hunter, and Shepherd Smith, National Association of Evangelicals, P.O. Box 28, Wheaton, IL 60189; 708/665-0500. Two audiotapes, $5.00 each.

LEADER'S GUIDE/CHAPTER 8

GOAL
To evaluate the condition of the American family and its Christian counterpart as it relates to the epidemic.

APPROACH (Choose one.)
1. Invite a counselor or pastor to present concerns he or she has on family stress and struggles in today's culture, as well as thoughts about how today's culture relates to the epidemic.
2. Ask class members to make presentations on family life from their perspectives, touching locally common family issues.

SCRIPTURES

1 Timothy 3; 5	Malachi 4:6
Matthew 15:1-9	Luke 11:5-13
Proverbs 13:1; 15:5	Ephesians 6:1-4
Colossians 3	1 Peter 3:1-7

PRAYER FOCUS
Families in our nation; organizations and ministries working to strengthen them; families in your church; your own family.

DISCUSSION QUESTIONS
1. List the pressures and strains on the American family today.
2. Explain the role of the family in the HIV epidemic.
3. Describe the godly family unit's actions and attitudes, based on Scripture.
4. How is the family unit in your church different from the ideal described in #3?
5. How is your family different from the ideal described in #3?
6. List some steps for your family to take to become more like the biblical pattern.

DISCUSSION/APPLICATION
Ask members to write down the areas of family life they personally struggle with most. Then ask them to list steps in a strategy to work on changing poor patterns to good ones. Finally, ask each group member to identify one person to approach who will keep him or her accountable for working to change specific behaviors and patterns.

RESOURCES
Gaining Through Losing by Evelyn Christenson (1980), Victor Books, Wheaton, Illinois.

The Key to Your Child's Heart by Gary Smalley (1984), Word Book Publishers, Waco, Texas.

Parenting Us: How God Does It by Karen and David Mains (1986), Harold Shaw Publishers, Wheaton, Illinois.

Parents in Pain by John White (1979), InterVarsity Press, Downers Grove, Illinois.

Plague in Our Midst: Sexuality, AIDS and the Christian Family by Gregg R. Albers, M.D. (1988), Huntington House, Lafayette, Louisiana.

The Sexual Christian by Tim Stafford (1989), Victor Books, Wheaton, Illinois.

Values Begin at Home by Ted Ward (1989), Victor Books, Wheaton, Illinois.

Where Does a Mother Go to Resign? by Barbara Johnson (1987), Bethany House, Minneapolis.

LEADER'S GUIDE/CHAPTER 9

GOAL
To face the reality of behaviors within the church that put individuals at risk for contracting HIV, as a step toward changing such behaviors, to begin to develop ways to prevent or change behaviors.

APPROACH (Choose one.)
1. Invite a representative from Teen Challenge, Youth for Christ, or another group active in your state to discuss behaviors prevalent among the youth with whom such groups work.
2. As a group, read the Josh McDowell survey on church youth sexual behaviors.
3. Ask a youth pastor or sponsor to share his or her knowledge about behavior patterns in churched youth.
4. Arrange for teens from a church other than your own to talk about sexual and drug activity from their perspective.

SCRIPTURE

Hosea	Romans 1:18–2:16; 6:1-4
Matthew 24:36-51	Galatians 6:7-10
2 Timothy 2:8-13; 3:1-9	Psalm 51

PRAYER FOCUS
All those in a cycle of behavior which puts them at risk for contracting HIV. Ministers, counselors, and others working to assist people to break destructive behavior cycles. Pray that young people and leaders in your church will face these issues openly and address them effectively.

DISCUSSION QUESTIONS
1. What factors have led to the present harmful behaviors among our nation's youth?
2. Who shares the responsibility and what should their roles be in helping reshape behavior?
3. What clues does a study of Hosea provide for us as we seek to change the destructive behavior patterns of those who know no better way?
4. What promises does God make to those who strive for righteousness and changed behaviors?

DISCUSSION/APPLICATION
Ask group members to inventory personal behaviors that they need to change so they will be modeling godly examples. Pray silently in the meeting about these personal lists.

OUTSIDE ACTIVITY
Talk to at least one high school or college student about sexual activity and drug use to discover their attitudes and opinions.

RESOURCES
The Addictive Personality: Understanding Compulsion in Our Lives by Craig Nakken (1988), Harper & Row, New York.

AIDS and Young People by Robert Redfield, M.D., and Wanda Kay Franz, Ph.D. (1988), Regnery Gateway, Inc. (available through Sex Respect, P.O. Box 97, Golf, IL 60029-0097); booklet, $3.50.

Drug-Proof Your Kids: A Prevention Guide and Intervention Plan by Stephen Arterburn and Jim Burns (1989), Focus on the Family Publishing, Pomona, California.

Eros Defiled by John White (1977), InterVarsity Press, Downers Grove, Illinois.

Raising a Child Conservatively in a Sexually Permissive World by S. Gordon and G. Gordon (1986), Simon & Schuster, New York.

The Sexual Christian by Tim Stafford (1989), Victor Books, Wheaton, Illinois.

Sexual Sanity by Earl D. Wilson (1984), InterVarsity Press, Downers Grove, Illinois.

The Snare by Lois Mowday (1988), NavPress, Colorado Springs, Colorado.

Smoke Screen by Betsy Tice White (1989), Abingdon Press, Nashville.

When Society Becomes an Addict by Anne Wilson Schaef (1987), Harper & Row, New York.

Your Child & Drugs: Help for Concerned Parents by Ross Campbell, M.D. (1988), Victor Books, Wheaton, Illinois.

LEADER'S GUIDE/CHAPTER 10

GOAL
To understand the critical and immediate role that prevention will play in curtailing the epidemic's spread; to learn where to find tools to institute prevention programs.

APPROACH (Choose one.)
1. Invite representatives from your church youth group, college-age group, and young single adults to discuss with your group members ways to formulate effective prevention messages that they, as young people, would listen to.
2. Invite a parent who has gone through an addiction, pregnancy, or other similar crisis with his or her child, relative, or friend. Ask the parent to explain how to deal with the consequences and to experience healing in spirit and relationships.
3. Play a video or audiotape on prevention of HIV infection to spur discussion.

SCRIPTURE

Ephesians 4–6	Romans 12:1-2
1 Peter 1:13-25; 2	Jeremiah 31:33-34
Hebrews 4:14-16	1 John 1:6-7; 2:4-6
1 Corinthians 5	1 Thessalonians 5:23
Psalm 103	

PRAYER FOCUS
For young people, parents, and those who work with families and youth, that they will have wisdom and sensitivity in approaching these difficult issues in the proper spirit. Pray also for those young people and adults putting themselves at risk for contracting HIV because of their behavior, that the Lord will send someone to help them change their patterns before it's too late.

DISCUSSION QUESTIONS
1. Evaluate what messages are currently being sent to youth in your church and in your family regarding godly behavior. How are they phrased? Are they effective?
2. Study the messages Scripture gives regarding sexual purity and keeping one's body healthy.
3. List scriptural elements that must be part of prevention messages.

DISCUSSION/APPLICATION
As a group, devise some effective prevention messages. Involve teens, college students, and adult singles too. Brainstorm ways

to use the messages in church programs and curricula.

RESOURCES
How to Help Your Child Say "No," Josh McDowell Ministries,
Dallas, Texas. Audiotape, $5.00.

*The Need to Educate Youth with a Clear Message of Preven-
tion* by Peggy Markell, R.N., ASAP. Audiotape, suggested contribution $6.00.

The Chastity Challenge, Respect, Inc., Bradley, Illinois. Videotape, 60 minutes.

Everyone Is Not Doing It, Project Respect, Golf, Illinois. Four-
tape video series.

How to Help Your Child Say "No" to Sexual Pressure, Josh
McDowell Ministries, Dallas, Texas. Eight-tape video series.

AIDS Prevention Program for Youth, American Red Cross,
Washington, D.C.

Changing Your Thought Patterns by George Sanchez,
NavPress, Colorado Springs, Colorado. Booklet.

Help Your Children Say No to Drugs by John Baucom (1987),
Zondervan Publishing House, Grand Rapids.

*Hooked on Life: How to Recover from Addiction and
Codependency* by Stephen Arterburn and Tim Timmons (1985),
Thomas Nelson Publishers, Nashville.

How to Say No to a Stubborn Habit by Erwin W. Lutzer (1979),
Victor Books, Wheaton, Illinois.

Kids Who Follow, Kids Who Don't by Ross Campbell, M.D.
(1989), Victor Books, Wheaton, Illinois.

LEADER'S GUIDE/CHAPTER 11

GOAL
To see how the biblical concept of suffering relates to those
infected, those affected, and those ministering.

APPROACH
1. Locate stories of early church martyrs, missionaries, and others who have suffered in their ministries, as a basis for discussion.
2. Ask members to share about times of suffering they have experienced and how they affected their families, their relationships with friends, and their faith.
3. Invite a member of your church or community who has lived under a repressive government to explain suffering from that perspective.

SCRIPTURE
Romans 5:1-5; 8:17-39   Job
Hebrews 2:10-18; 13:1-3   1 Peter 4:12
Philippians 3:1-10   1 Corinthians 12:26

PRAYER FOCUS
All who suffer in the world, the nation, your community, your church, your family. And for an understanding of how suffering is a part of our faith.

DISCUSSION QUESTIONS
1. What kinds of suffering can we expect to see from the AIDS epidemic for: those infected, families, leaders, society at large?
2. How does Scripture's discussion of suffering apply to this epidemic?
3. List sacrifices we could make to alleviate future suffering.
4. What is each Christian's role in the suffering of the AIDS epidemic?

DISCUSSION/APPLICATION
Develop a strategy as a group for ways the church and individual Christians can start now to lessen future suffering.

RESOURCES
Counseling the Terminally Ill and Grieving by Gregg Albers, M.D. (1989), Word Publishing, Waco, Texas.

Disappointment with God by Philip Yancey (1988), Zondervan Publishing House, Grand Rapids, Michigan.

The Spiritual Needs of Children by Judith Allen Shelly (1982), InterVarsity Press, Downers Grove, Illinois.

When Someone Asks for Help by Everett L. Worthington, Jr. (1982), InterVarsity Press, Downers Grove, Illinois.

When They All Go Home: What to Do After the Funeral by Robert V. Dodd (1989), Abingdon Press, Nashville.

Where Is God When It Hurts? by Philip Yancey (1977), Zondervan Publishing Co., Grand Rapids.

LEADER'S GUIDE/CHAPTER 12

GOAL
To face and work to eliminate prejudices which may be keeping us from ministry related to AIDS or other issues.

APPROACH
1. Role play situations in which prejudice is shown by a Christian against another Christian or unchurched individual.
2. Ask group members to share times when they have felt prejudice directed against them and how it affected them emotionally and spiritually.

SCRIPTURE
1 Corinthians 4:5-13; 13:1-13	Ecclesiastes 7:20
1 John 2:9-11; 3:17-18	Proverbs 16:2, 5, 18-19
Mark 2:16-17	Matthew 7:1-14; 9:13;
Luke 19:1-10	18:21-35
James 1:22; 2; 4:11-12; 5:9	Luke 7:36-39, 44-48, 50

PRAYER FOCUS
Personal areas of prejudice or bias.

DISCUSSION QUESTIONS
1. List prejudices commonly seen or felt within the church.
2. Study Scripture to discover:
   A. the root of prejudice
   B. God's perspective on prejudice
3. Discuss specific struggles in overcoming prejudices — obstacles that need to be removed.
4. Find Scripture to assist you in breaking down the barriers.

DISCUSSION/APPLICATION
List areas where you personally are prejudiced. Spend time praying for yourself and fellow believers that God would enable you all to deal with any such biases that would stand in the way of ministry.

OUTSIDE ACTIVITY
Actively work at using behavior change skills discussed earlier to reform patterns of prejudicial or judgmental attitudes and actions.

RESOURCES
A Forgiving God in an Unforgiving World by Ron Lee Davis (1984), Harvest House, Eugene, Oregon.

A Step Further by Joni Eareckson and Steve Estes (1978), Zondervan Publishing House, Grand Rapids.

The Christian Mindset in a Secular Society by Carl F.H. Henry (1984), Multnomah, Portland, Oregon.

When Life Isn't Fair by Dwight Carlson, M.D. and Susan Carlson Wood (1989), Harvest House, Eugene, Oregon.

Exodus International, P.O. Box 2121, San Rafael, CA 94912, 415/454-1017. This is a worldwide network of Christian organizations which minister to those overcoming homosexuality and other life-dominating sexual problems.

LEADER'S GUIDE/CHAPTER 13

GOAL
To determine personal commitment to ministry in general and to AIDS-related ministry in specific.

APPROACH (Choose one.)
1. Spend the session developing a worship liturgy and service to be held in your church to raise AIDS awareness.
2. Reflect on studied materials. Ask members to share how their attitudes have changed since the beginning of the study; what specific personal commitments they will make to continued involvement with the AIDS issue; any concerns still not resolved.
3. Determine a project which the group or individual members could promote church-wide in order to raise funds for AIDS ministry.
4. Play a videotape not previously seen as a summary, challenging group members to solidify changes in attitude, action, or lifestyle that they feel they should make.

SCRIPTURE
    Proverbs 16:7   Micah 6:8
    Psalm 145:8-21   Ephesians 4
    Romans 12   1 Corinthians 12
    1 Kings 3:5-9

PRAYER FOCUS
All the individuals mentioned in the book who are dealing personally with HIV infection or AIDS; the AIDS organizations and ministries mentioned; national leaders on the issue in medicine, public policy, economics, and the church. The current political administration in planning strategy to cope with the disease. Your family, your church, yourself: for protection, wisdom, compassion, and guidance.

RESOURCES
Against the Night: Living in the New Dark Ages by Charles Colson (1989), Servant Books, Ann Arbor, Michigan.

How to Help the Hurting by Everett L. Worthington, Jr. (1985), InterVarsity Press, Downers Grove, Illinois.

Parents Passing on the Faith by Carl K. Spackman (1989), Victor Books, Wheaton, Illinois.

The Samaritan Strategy by Colonel V. Doner (1988), Woglemuth & Hyatt Publishers, Inc., Brentwood, Tennessee.

GLOSSARY
AIDS/HIV Terms

AIDS — Acquired Immunodeficiency Syndrome. The symptomatic stage of disease of people who are infected with the Human Immunodeficiency Virus (HIV). The term AIDS is decreasingly used in medical settings, being replaced by HIV.

Anonymous test sites — Testing centers established by many state public health departments where individuals can go to be tested for HIV without identifying themselves by name to anyone, and where the results of the tests are not recorded.

Antibodies — Molecules produced by the immune system to respond to specific foreign agents in the bloodstream in order to eliminate them from the body. Because of their particular characteristics, the antibodies that are formed in response to HIV allow for testing for the presence of the virus.

Antigen — Molecule which induces the formation of an antibody.

Asymptomatic — Refers to individuals who are HIV positive but have no symptoms of HIV or AIDS and are otherwise apparently healthy.

Bisexual — Individual who has sexual contact with members of both sexes.

Boarder babies — HIV positive infants abandoned by their mothers and left in hospitals to live out their lives.

Centers for Disease Control (CDC) — Primary government agency under the Department of Health and Human Services which has responsibility for monitoring disease spread and developing prevention strategies for infectious diseases, including the HIV virus.

Cytomegalovirus — One of a group of herpes viruses that infect man, monkeys, and rodents.

Discordant couple—Sexual or IV partners in which one individual is HIV positive and the other is HIV negative.

Doubling time—Length of time required for either HIV infections or symptomatic AIDS cases to double in number.

Dynamic infectivity—Theory that states the longer an individual is infected with HIV, the more infectious he or she becomes to others through increased amounts of virus present in body fluids.

Epidemiology—The study of the relationships of various factors determining the frequency and distribution of diseases in a human environment.

Etiology—The study of factors that cause disease.

Food and Drug Administration (FDA)—Government agency responsible for approval of drugs used in treating HIV infection or opportunistic infections which appear in patients during the symptomatic stage, or AIDS.

Gay—Homosexual man.

Hemophiliac—Individual whose blood lacks the ability to clot without additional injections of a concentrated blood-clotting agent called Factor VIII.

Heterosexual—Individual who has intercourse with only the opposite sex.

HIV—Human Immunodeficiency Virus, the virus which infects individuals and ultimately causes the symptomatic disease known as AIDS.

Homosexual—Man or woman who engages in sexual activity exclusively with members of the same sex.

Immune system—Body's internal natural defense mechanism against foreign agents which protects it from acquiring disease; concentrated in white blood cells, primarily T4 lymphocytes, macrophages, and monocytes.

Intercourse—Intimate sexual contact involving the genitalia.

Intimate sexual contact—Sexual activity between members of the opposite sex or same sex in which body fluids are exchanged.

IV-drug user—Individual who injects drugs into his or her body through the veins.

Kaposi's sarcoma—Cancer or tumor of the blood and/or lymphatic vessel walls.

Lentivirus—Virus that can cross the blood/brain barrier, destroy brain tissue, and remain in the body in a chronic subclinical state for long periods of time.

Lesbian—Woman who has intimate sexual contact only with other women.

Lymph node—Small, simple lymph gland which, when swollen, is the most common symptom of early-stage disease.

Lymphadenopathy—Disease of the lymph nodes.

Lymphocyte—Primary "foot soldier" of the body's immune system; a type of white blood cell.

Macrophage—White blood cell which is part of the body's immune defense system as well as primary target and host cell for HIV.

Mandatory HIV testing—Required testing for HIV virus whether the individual agrees to it or not.

Monocyte—White blood cell which is part of the body's immune defense system as well as primary target and host cell for HIV.

Monogamy—Practice of maintaining in marriage only one intimate sexual partner.

Multiple partners—More than one sexual partner either during the same period of time or consecutively.

Needle-sticks—In the health-care setting, the inadvertent pricking of health-care personnel with needles in the process of performing their duties.

Opportunistic infection—Infection caused by an organism that rarely causes disease in persons with healthy immune systems, but which attacks immuno-compromised persons.

Oral—Refers to the oral cavity or mouth.

Partner notification—Program wherein sexual or IV-drug partners are confidentially informed of their exposure to a communicable disease.

Premarital HIV testing—Testing of individuals considering marriage for disclosure of HIV infection.

Premarital sex—Intimate sexual relations before marriage.

Promiscuity—Consistent intimate sexual contact with multiple partners.

PWA—Person with AIDS.

Reverse transcriptase—Enzyme used to make DNA in a cell cytoplasm, and derived from the RNA of the virus.

Safe sex—Now referred to as "safer sex," which is sexual contact using barrier protection (e.g., condoms).

Seroconversion—Initial development of antibodies to a specific antigen.

Serologic—Relating to blood serum.

Seropositive—Refers to individual whose blood test shows antibodies to HIV are present, indicating that the person is infected with HIV.

Seroprevalence—Distribution of a specific antigen within a population based on blood serum tests.

STDs—Sexually transmitted diseases, which include syphilis, gonorrhea, herpes, chlamydia, and HIV infection among others; also called venereal diseases.

Swingers—Individuals who often exchange sexual partners.

Systemic infection—Infection throughout the entire body.

T cell—Small white blood cell that triggers and participates in the body's immune defense; also known as T-lymphocyte or T4.

Testing—Serological diagnosis of HIV.

Transmission—Act of passing the virus from an infected individual to an uninfected individual.

Vaccine—Preventive treatment which keeps individuals from acquiring diseases.

WHO—World Health Organization.

ENDNOTES

CHAPTER 7

1. *Time*, October 9, 1989, "Nobody's Children," p. 91.

2. *New York Times*, July 17, 1989, "AIDS Legacy: a Growing Generation of Orphans," p. A1.

3. *New York Times*, October 8, 1989, "AIDS Is Spreading in Teen-agers, A New Trend Alarming to Experts," p. 1.

4. *The National Network*, October 1988, "The Covenant House Study." The National Network of Runaway Youth Services, Inc., Washington, D.C.

5. *Foursquare World Advance*, March/April 1987, "Hoping Against Hope."

CHAPTER 8

1. Family Research Council press release, November 17, 1989.

2. *The American Family Under Siege* (Family Research Council: Washington, D.C., 1989), p. 1.

3. *Newsweek*, Winter/Spring 1990, "What Happened to the Family?" p. 16.

4. *Newsweek*, Winter/Spring 1990, "Step by Step," p. 30.

5. *The American Family Under Siege*, p. 1.

6. *Ibid.*, p. 5.

7. *The Washington Times*, November 9, 1989, "Single Parent Poverty," p. F2.

8. *Newsweek*, Winter/Spring 1990, "The New Untouchables," p. 48.

9. *The Washington Post*, December 10, 1989, "The Decade By the Numbers," p. A20.

10. "The New Untouchables," p. 48.

11. *The American Family Under Siege*, p. 6.

12. *Ibid.*, p. 15.

13. *The American Family Under Siege*, p. 18.

14. *Newsweek*, Winter/Spring 1990, "Young Beyond Their Years," p. 60.

15. *Ibid.*

16. *The Washington Times*, November 9, 1989, "Single Parent Poverty," p. F2.

17. Ross Campbell, *Kids Who Follow, Kids Who Don't* (Wheaton, Ill.: Victor Books, 1989), p. 14.

18. *Ibid.*, p. 137.

19. *Newsweek*, Winter/Spring 1990, "What Happened to the Family?" p. 17.

20. *The Connecticut Mutual Life Report on American Values in the '80s: The Impact of Belief* (Hartford, Conn.: Connecticut Mutual Life Insurance Co., 1981).

21. Ted Ward, *Values Begin at Home* (Wheaton, Ill.: Victor Books, 1989), p. 27.

22. *Ibid.*, pp. 33–35.

23. Campbell, p. 138.

CHAPTER 9
1. *The Washington Times*, November 9, 1989, "More Employees Seeking Alcohol and Drug Counseling," p. B5.

2. *Newsweek*, February 20, 1989, "Roots of Addiction," p. 52.

3. *The Washington Times*, December 19, 1989, "Drug-use rate found higher in white than black youth," p. A5.

4. Stephen Arterburn and Jim Burns, *Drug-Proof Your Kids* (Pomona, Calif.: Focus on the Family Publishers, 1989), p. 5.

5. *What You Can Do About Drug Use in America*, Department of Health and Human Services, DHHS Publication No. (ADM) 88-1572 (1988), p. 17.

6. *Newsweek*, September 25, 1989, "So Little Time, So Many Cases."

7. *Time*, December 8, 1985, "Children Having Children," p. 79.

8. *Ibid.*

9. *Newsweek*, Winter/Spring 1990, "Young Beyond Their Years," p. 54.

10. *The Miami Herald*, February 27, 1989, "Study: Teens feel entitled to sex," p. 10A.

11. *Teen Sex Survey in the Evangelical Church, Executive Summary Report* (Dallas: Josh McDowell Ministries, 1987).

12. *Christianity Today*, July 14, 1989, "Abortion: Common at Christian Colleges?" p. 42.

CHAPTER 10
1. *New York Times*, November 24, 1989, "Panel Warns of Failures in Efforts to Halt AIDS."

2. Margaret A. Fischl et al. "Evaluation of Heterosexual Partners, Children, and Household Contacts of Adults with AIDS," *Journal of the American Medical Association*, February 6, 1987.

3. *AIDS Education for Substance Abusers*, research study conducted by Greenwich House, Inc., 1988.

4. C.S. Lewis, *Mere Christianity* (New York: Macmillan Publishing Co., 1943) pp. 92–93.

CHAPTER 11
1. Dietrich Bonhoeffer, *The Cost of Discipleship* (New York: Macmillan Publishing Co., 1963) pp. 96, 101.

2. Helmut Thielicke, *The Faith Letters* (Waco, Texas: Word Books Publisher, 1978), p. 33.

CHAPTER 12
1. C.S. Lewis, *Mere Christianity* (New York: Macmillan Publishing Co., 1943) pp. 94–95.

AIDS/HIV-RELATED MINISTRIES

NATIONAL MINISTRIES

AIDS Crisis and Christians Today (ACCT)
P.O. Box 24647
Nashville, TN 37202-4647
615/385-ACCT

AIS Information Ministries
P.O. Box 136116
Ft. Worth, TX 76136
817/237-0230

Christian AIDS Services Alliance (CASA)
P.O. Box 23277
Washington, D.C. 20026
1-800/FOR-CASA

Family Matters, Inc.
P.O. Box 621101
Littleton, CO 80162
303/973-4758

Love & Action, Inc.
3 Church Circle, #8
Annapolis, MD 21401
301/268-3442

REGIONAL/LOCAL MINISTRIES

California
AIDS Resource Ministry (ARM)
12488 Venice Blvd.
Los Angeles, CA 90066
213/572-0140

Ariel House
P.O. Box 202010
San Diego, CA 92120
619/698-1560

The Bridge
1759 Oak St.
San Francisco, CA 94118
415/552-AIDS

Beyond Rejection (regional)
P.O. Box 2154
Hemet, CA 92343
714/925-0028
Hot line: 1-800/966-AIDS

Beyond Rejection (local)
P.O. Box 589
Long Beach, CA 90801
213/599-1316

Christian AIDS Network
1020 E. McKinley
Fresno, CA 93728
209/264-6125

Lifeline AIDS Network
P.O. Box 3694
San Rafael, CA 94912
415/454-0960

Florida
Eleutheros
1298 Minnesota Ave., Suite D
Winter Park, FL 32789
407/629-5770

Solomon's Porch
P.O. Box 541157
Orlando, FL 32854

Victory House
3601 Davie Blvd.
Ft. Lauderdale, FL 33312
305/463-0848

Georgia
GS Project
P.O. Box 900211
Atlanta, GA 30329
404/873-4589

Illinois
ACTION
5445 N. Clark St.
Chicago, IL 60640
312/334-5159

AIDS Pastoral Care Network
2035 N. Lincoln Ave.
Chicago, IL 60614
312/975-5180

Beyond Rejection
P.O. Box 156
Rockford, IL 61105
815/963-0303

Love & Action, Inc.
Chicago Area Representatives
107 S. Hi Lusi
Mt. Prospect, IL 60056
708/392-3123

Massachusetts
Beyond Rejection
P.O. Box 3188
Andover, MA 01840
508/685-5577

Michigan
ARISE
Ward Presbyterian Church
1700 Farmington Rd.
Livonia, MI 48154
313/422-1826

New Jersey
Arise & Shine Ministries for Children
P.O. Box 526
Belleville, NJ 07109
201/450-0349

New York
Footprints Ministry
560 W. 43rd, Ste. 9-H
New York, NY 10036
201/268-7210

Love & Action, Inc.
New York Area Representatives
Brooklyn, NY
718/435-1958

North Carolina
Love & Action, Inc.
Area Representatives
Fayetteville, NC
919/867-1800

Ohio
Prodigal Ministries
P.O. Box 19949
Cincinnati, OH 45219-0949

Oklahoma
First Stone Ministries
P.O. Box 1367
Bethany, OK 73008
405/720-2437

Restoration Outreach
2800 Center/E. Shelly Dr., Ste. 818
Tulsa, OK 74105
918/744-0437

Pennsylvania
AMORE
P.O. Box 342
Bethlehem, PA 18016-0342
215/866-5824

HOPE
Tenth Presbyterian Church
1701 Delancey Pl.
Philadelphia, PA 19103
215/735-4673

Love & Action, Inc.
Area Representatives
Lancaster County, PA
717/560-9081

Tennessee
BEYOND Fear
P.O. Box 60383
Nashville, TN 37206
615/254-8341

Texas
CARE
Fellowship Bible Church of Park Cities
8202 Boedeker
Dallas, TX 75225
214/404-0283 and 214/824-1178

Washington
Living Hope
P.O. Box 23198
Seattle, WA 98102
206/324-0208

Open Arms
P.O. Box 611
Spokane, WA 99210-0611
509/484-2437

ASAP maintains an up-to-date list of ministries as we learn
of them or as new ones are formed. For additional information on ministries in your area, contact:
Americans for a Sound AIDS/HIV Policy (ASAP)
P.O. Box 17433
Washington, D.C. 20041
703/471-7350